Titrimetric Analy
for A and S Leve__

SI Edition

J. G. Stark
M.A. (Cantab.), Head of Chemistry, Glasgow Academy

John Murray   50 Albemarle Street   London

Also by J. G. Stark

Questions and Problems in Inorganic Chemistry
Chemistry Data Book (with H. G. Wallace)
Experiments in Organic Chemistry
  (Ernst Otto – translated and revised)
Basic Chemistry Data Book
Comprehension Exercises for Advanced Chemistry Courses
Advanced Chemistry Multiple Choice Tests

Printed and bound in Hong Kong
by Wing King Tong Co Ltd

0 7195 2446 6

Contents

Preface

This book is intended for the use of those who are preparing for A level and open scholarship practical examinations. The 'molarity' method of calculation is used throughout so that the book will be suitable for use in connection with the new A level practical syllabuses. The principles and experimental methods of titrimetric analysis are discussed in a short introductory chapter and succeeding chapters deal with acid-base, redox, precipitation and complexometric titrations in turn. A short final chapter provides an introduction to conductometric and potentiometric titrations as examples of end-point detection using physical properties.

Each chapter begins with a brief theoretical introduction and includes full experimental instructions for a wide range of determinations. Additional exercises of an investigatory nature and worked examples are also included in most chapters. Suggestions for further reading are given at the end of each chapter to help the student who may not be familiar with the theoretical principles involved in the various types of titration and for the use of the student who wishes to read more widely in this field.

The author wishes to thank his wife for typing the manuscript and Mr H. G. Wallace, formerly Head of the Chemistry Department at St Mary's College, Liverpool, for reading the proofs.

J. G. S.

SI Units

The SI unit of concentration is mole per cubic metre. However, in titrimetric analysis a decimal fraction of this unit – mole per litre (cubic decimetre) – is more convenient. The symbol M is used for mol l^{-1} throughout this book.

The physical quantity 'molarity' (symbol M) is retained, but it should strictly be called *concentration* (expressed in mol l^{-1}). Also, the physical quantity 'weight', which has been used in the past where mass is correct, should now be replaced by *mass*. The obsolete term 'normality' (symbol N) is still used in some schools and it is, therefore, briefly discussed in this book.

1 Titrimetric Analysis: Principles and Experimental Methods

Methods of Analysis

The identification of a substance is known as *qualitative analysis* which includes, for example, the elements present in an organic compound or the components of a given mixture. *Quantitative analysis* involves the determination of the quantities of these components present and may be carried out in one of two main ways:

(*a*) by weighing – *gravimetric analysis,* which is capable of a high degree of accuracy;

(*b*) by the measurement of the volumes of either gases or solutions – *volumetric analysis.* This includes methods in which a certain volume of one solution contained in a burette is added to a known volume of another until all the second reagent has reacted. This operation is an example of *titrimetric analysis,* which is more rapid than gravimetric analysis.

Instrumental methods of analysis are now used extensively, as they generally require smaller amounts of material than the methods which are considered in this book. These involve the use of such instruments as pH meters, colorimeters, spectrophotometers and polarographic instruments. The use of physical properties such as conductivity and e.m.f. in titrimetric analysis is briefly considered at the end of this book.

Titrimetric Analysis

The process of adding a measured volume of one reagent to a known volume of a second reagent until the reaction is complete is known as a *titration* and the aim of this process is to determine the stoichiometric (or equivalence) point of the reaction. This is often done by means of the change of colour of an *indicator* which has been added. Titrimetric analysis is essentially a method for determining the concentration of an unknown solution using two solutions which react together according to a known stoichiometric equation. At the stoichiometric point the reaction has taken place exactly according to this equation, so that neither of the two reagents is in an excess. If the concentration of one of the solutions is known, say that in the burette, then the concentration of the second, an accurately measured volume of which is transferred to the titration flask by means of a pipette, can be calculated from the volumes of the reacting solutions at the stoichiometric point and from the relevant equation for the reaction.

An indicator is usually added to the solution to detect the stoichiometric point. It changes colour when an excess of the reagent added from the burette is present. This is known as the *end-point* of the titration and, ideally, it coincides with the stoichiometric point. The difference between the end-point and the stoichiometric point is known as the *titration error,* which must be kept as low as possible.

An important variation of this method is known as *back-titration,* in which a solution of one reagent reacts with a known excess of a second reagent, the excess of which is determined by titration with a suitable reagent of known concentration.

The four main types of titration are:
(*a*) acid-base titrations,
(*b*) redox titrations,
(*c*) prccipitation titrations,
(*d*) complexometric titrations.

Molarities, Normalities and Equivalents

The concentration of a solution can be expressed in a number of ways, e.g.
(*a*) as the weight of solute dissolved in a stated volume of solution (grams per litre),
(*b*) as the *molarity* (M), involving the molecular (or formula) weight of the solute,
(*c*) as the *normality* (N), involving the equivalent weight of the solute.

Method (*a*) is the simplest in practice and is used for making a standard solution by the direct weighing of a primary standard (see p. 4). Method (*b*) depends directly on the chemical equation for the reaction involved in the titration, i.e.

$$a\text{A} + b\text{B} \rightarrow \text{products} \qquad (1)$$

in which a moles of A react stoichiometrically with b moles of B. A *one molar* solution (1 M) contains one mole, i.e. the molecular (or formula) weight in grams, of solute in one litre of solution.

To obtain the concentration as molarity of an unknown solution from the volumes of reacting solutions, the equation for the reaction is used as follows.

If M_A, M_B are the molarities of the solutions containing A and B respectively, and V_A, V_B are the volumes of the solutions of A and B respectively, then at the stoichiometric (or equivalence) point, according to equation (1), a moles of A react with b moles of B and

$$\frac{\text{Number of moles of A}}{\text{Number of moles of B}} = \frac{M_A V_A/1000}{M_B V_B/1000} = \frac{a}{b}$$

$$\therefore M_A = M_B \cdot \frac{V_B}{V_A} \cdot \frac{a}{b} \qquad (2)$$

and, concentration of A in g l^{-1} = M_A × molecular weight of A.

In method (c), it must be remembered that a *normality* is meaningless unless stated in the context of a particular reaction. A *one normal* solution (1 N) contains one 1 g equiv, i.e. the equivalent weight in grams, of solute in one litre of solution. Similarly, a decinormal solution (0·1 N) contains 0·1 g equiv per l.

According to the law of equivalents, 1 g equiv of A will react stoichiometrically with 1 g equiv of B, so that equal volumes of equinormal solutions will react stoichiometrically. This is the main reason for the use of the concept of normality. To obtain the concentration as normality of an unknown solution from the volumes of reacting solutions the following calculation is carried out.

If N_A, N_B are the normalities of the solutions containing A and B respectively, and V_A, V_B are the volumes of the solutions of A and B respectively, then at the stoichiometric point

$$\text{number of g equiv of A} = \frac{N_A V_A}{1000} = \text{number of g equiv of B} = \frac{N_B V_B}{1000}$$

$$\therefore N_A = N_B \cdot \frac{V_B}{V_A} \qquad (3)$$

and, concentration of A in g l^{-1} = N_A × equivalent weight of A.

Equation (2) in terms of molarities and equation (3) in terms of normalities give the same result.

Stoichiometric Coefficients

When the molarity method for expressing concentrations is used, the values of a and b must be known (see equation (2)). However, if the normality method is used, $\frac{a}{b}$ must still be known even though a and b do not appear in equation (3), as the equivalent weight has to be calculated from the molecular weight. It can readily be shown that

$$\frac{\text{Equivalent weight of A}}{\text{Equivalent weight of B}} = \frac{\text{Molecular weight of A}}{\text{Molecular weight of B}} \cdot \frac{a}{b}$$

Comparison of Molarities and Normalities

The main advantage of the normality method is that equation (3) is simpler than (2), so that a simple 1 : 1 ratio is obtained for all reactions of the same type, e.g. acid-base reactions. However, a given reagent may react in different ways so that, although its gram-molecular weight has a constant value, its gram-equivalent weight depends on the particular reaction in which it is involved. For example, potassium hydrogen oxalate can react as a monobasic acid:

$$KHC_2O_4 \rightarrow K^+ + H^+ + C_2O_4^{2-}$$

with an equivalent weight equal to its molecular weight. However, it can also act as a reducing agent, e.g. with potassium permanganate:

$$KHC_2O_4 \rightarrow K^+ + H^+ + 2CO_2 + 2e^-$$

when its equivalent weight is equal to *half* its molecular weight. This means that a solution of potassium hydrogen oxalate which is 0·1 N as an acid will be 0·2 N as a reducing agent. The solution is, of course, 0·1 M with respect to KHC_2O_4 in both reactions.

Standards

Titrimetric analysis is essentially a comparative method of analysis. A reference solution of known concentration is necessary if the concentrations of other solutions are required. A *standard solution*, of known concentration (in g l^{-1}), is made by dissolving an accurately known weight of a *primary standard* in a known volume of solution.

A primary standard is a substance which satisfies the following requirements:

(*a*) it must be readily available in a state of high purity;

(*b*) it should be stable in air at ordinary temperatures, so that it can be stored indefinitely without change in composition and weighed without special precautions, e.g. to exclude moisture;

(*c*) it should be readily soluble in water; and

(*d*) it should have a high equivalent weight to reduce the effects of small errors in weighing. Although pure electrolytic silver is often used as an ultimate reference standard, the following substances are commonly used as primary standards.

Acid-base titrations	Sodium carbonate, borax, constant boiling-point hydrochloric acid, and sulphamic acid (NH_2SO_3H)
Redox titrations	Sodium oxalate, potassium dichromate, potassium iodate, iodine, and arsenic(III) oxide
Precipitation titrations	Sodium chloride
Complexometric titrations	Disodium ethylenediamine tetra-acetate dihydrate (disodium salt of EDTA)

Indicators

An indicator is a substance used in titrations, which has one colour in the presence of an excess of one reagent and a different colour in the presence of an excess of the other. In general, the indicator reacts in a similar way to the substance being titrated.

(a) An *acid-base indicator* is a weak organic acid or base. The two forms in which it can exist represent an acid and its conjugate base,* i.e.

$$HInd \rightleftharpoons H^+ + Ind^-$$
$$\text{colour } (1) \qquad \text{colour } (2)$$

The ionisation (or dissociation) constant, K_i, of the indicator is given by the equation

$$K_i = \frac{[H^+][Ind^-]}{[HInd]}$$

At the end-point the concentrations of the two coloured forms of the indicator are assumed to be equal

$$\text{i.e. } [Ind^-] = [HInd]$$
$$\therefore [H^+] = K_i$$

For example, methyl orange is red in the acid form (HInd), yellow in the basic form (Ind⁻) and orange when the concentrations of the two forms are equal. For the structural changes responsible for the colour change of the indicator, consult a textbook of organic chemistry, e.g. T. A. Geissman, *Principles of Organic Chemistry*, pp. 636, 666 (Freeman, 3rd ed., 1968).

It is possible to obtain a sharper colour change by using a mixture of an indicator and an inert dye. An example is screened methyl orange in which xylene cyanol FF (a blue dye) is added to methyl orange, giving a green colour in alkaline solution, red in acidic solution and grey in neutral solution.

Some indicators commonly used in acid-base titrations are shown in Table 1.

TABLE 1. ACID-BASE INDICATORS

Indicator	Colour change (acid → alkali)	pH range	Type of acid-base titration
Methyl orange	red *to* yellow	3·1–4·4	Strong acid—strong or weak base
Screened methyl orange	red *to* green	3·1–4·4	
Methyl red	red *to* yellow	4·4–6·2	
Phenolphthalein	colourless *to* red	8·3–10·0	Strong base—strong or weak acid

Note. There is no suitable indicator for a titration involving a weak acid and a weak base.

*According to the Brönsted-Lowry theory of acids and bases an acid is a substance which can act as a proton *donor*, e.g. $HCl + H_2O \rightleftharpoons H_3O^+ + Cl^-$, while a base is a substance which can act as a proton *acceptor*, e.g. Cl^-, which is known as the *conjugate base* of the acid HCl. The hydrogen ion is, in fact, hydrated (i.e. H_3O^+), though it is often convenient to represent it simply as H^+ (see page 10).

It will be seen that different indicators change colour over different pH ranges: the pH scale is a convenient way of representing the hydrogen ion concentration of a solution logarithmically, so that, if $[H^+] = 10^{-x}$ mol l^{-1}, then pH = x, i.e.

$$pH = -\log_{10}[H^+]$$

Note that increasing pH corresponds to *decreasing* hydrogen ion concentration.

(b) A *redox indicator* is oxidised or reduced with a consequent change in colour. An example of this is the use of an aqueous solution of barium diphenylamine p-sulphonate in the presence of phosphoric acid for the determination of iron(II) ions by potassium dichromate. The green colour of the solution changes sharply at the end-point to a deep violet colour.

(c) A *precipitation indicator* is a substance which has a certain colour in solution and is precipitated in the presence of the reagent added from the burette during the titration. The precipitate has a distinctive colour. Alternatively, an adsorption indicator may be used in titrations of this type. This is an organic dye which is adsorbed on the precipitate at the end-point with a consequent change in colour.

(d) A *complexometric indicator*, a coloured ligand,* forms a complex of distinctive colour with metal ions:

$$M^{n+} + lL \rightarrow ML_l^{n+}$$

The commonest indicator used in EDTA titrations is Eriochrome Black T, an azo dye, which is blue in the free state and red when complexed with a metal ion. The indicator and titrating reagent compete for the metal ion, both forming co-ordination compounds. The metal-indicator complex is stable, but less so than the metal-EDTA complex and the colour change occurs when the indicator co-ordinates to the metal ion.

Experimental Methods

The basic practical operations involved are:

(a) the transfer of a known volume of a solution containing an unknown weight of one reagent to a conical flask using a pipette (or a burette when the substance is poisonous),

(b) the addition of a suitable indicator to this solution, and

(c) the controlled addition of a solution containing a known weight of a second reagent from a burette until the reaction is complete.

To prepare a standard solution by direct weighing, the primary standard should be weighed in a weighing bottle which is first weighed empty (approximately), and then accurately with the amount of solid required. The solid is then transferred to a graduated flask through a funnel by tipping the weighing bottle, and the bottle (containing a small amount

*A *ligand* is an atom or group of atoms with an unshared electron pair which can, therefore, readily form co-ordinate linkages, e.g. NH_3, CN^-, EDTA.

of residual solid) is reweighed. The weight of solid used is then obtained by difference. All solid must be carefully washed from the funnel into the flask and dissolved in distilled water. The solution is then made up to the mark with distilled water, the last few cm³ being added by pipette. The contents must be thoroughly mixed to obtain a uniform solution before use.

Distilled water should always be used in the preparation of standard solutions.

Alternatively, many titrimetric reagents are available in concentrated form which can be diluted as directed to give a solution of specified molarity.

A *graduated flask* is calibrated to *contain* a specified volume of solution and is used to prepare standard solutions as described above.

A *pipette* with a bulb marked 'D' *delivers* a specified volume of solution, e.g. 20 or 25 cm³. There should be no air bubbles and it should be allowed to drain for approximately 15 seconds after the continuous flow of solution has stopped, without any acceleration of the process by blowing or tapping against the side of the conical flask. A careful note of the capacity of the pipette should always be made.

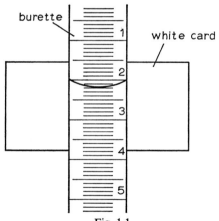

Fig. 1.1

A *burette* usually has a capacity of 50 cm³ and is graduated in 0·1 cm³. It is relatively easy to estimate 0·05 cm³ by eye. It is designed to deliver any volume of solution up to 50 cm³. The top level of the solution in the burette is called the *meniscus* and it is best to read the bottom of the meniscus with the aid of a white card or piece of paper held behind the burette (Fig. 1.1). It is advisable to check that the tap is functioning correctly before use. After washing and rinsing, the burette is nearly filled with the solution, the tap is opened and the solution is run out until all air bubbles have been expelled. If a funnel is used for filling the burette, it should be removed before beginning the titration. The burette must be vertical when the initial reading is taken: this need not be zero.

All graduated apparatus must be scrupulously clean if reproducible results are to be obtained. Burettes and pipettes should be washed with water and then with a small quantity of the solution they are to contain.* Graduated flasks and conical flasks should be washed with water only: any remaining water will not affect the total number of moles of reagent subsequently added.

Note. Graduated apparatus must *never be heated* in any way.

Readings should always be taken with the eye-level adjusted so that the front and back parts of the appropriate graduation appear to be coincident.

During the actual titration, the conical flask is placed on a white surface and it should be held close to the burette to minimise losses by splashing. The contents of the conical flask should be continuously swirled to avoid any local excess of the reagent added from the burette. If a burette with a glass tap is used, the tap should be held in the left hand (if the operator is right-handed) and the flask in the right hand to prevent loss of solution through the tap. As the end-point is approached, local momentary colour changes characteristic of the indicator usually appear in the solution. The walls of the conical flask should be washed with water from a wash bottle at this stage and the titration continued with the addition of the solution from the burette one drop at a time until the end-point is reached.

One trial and at least two accurate readings should be taken. Consecutive titrations should agree to within 0·05 cm³.† The conical flask should be thoroughly rinsed after each titration.

Standard solutions should be used economically—do not take more than is required from stock. Residues of expensive chemicals such as silver salts should be placed in the residues bottle provided.

Practical Notebooks

A careful record of each experiment should be kept in a suitable note-book All results should be recorded in detail and written down as soon as they are obtained. The written record should include:

(*a*) a statement of the principle of the experiment,

(*b*) a brief account of the experimental operations,

(*c*) the results presented where possible in tabular and graphical form,

(*d*) the method of calculation,

(*e*) a discussion of the results (including sources of error) and any conclusions which may be drawn from them.

*If a burette has been used with caustic alkali, it must be thoroughly washed after use with water, dilute acid and then more water.

†The volume of one drop delivered by an ordinary burette is about 0·05 cm³.

Specimen account: Preparation of a standard solution of sodium thio-sulphate using potassium iodate

Principle

A standard solution of potassium iodate is prepared and 25 cm³ aliquot parts are reacted with an excess of acidified potassium iodide solution:

$$IO_3^- + 5I^- + 6H^+ \rightarrow 3I_2 + 3H_2O \tag{1}$$
$$I_2 + I^- \rightarrow I_3^-$$

The liberated iodine is then titrated with the sodium thiosulphate solution, using starch as indicator:

$$I_3^- + 2S_2O_3^{2-} \rightarrow 3I^- + S_4O_6^{2-} \tag{2}$$

Results

Weight of weighing bottle empty	$= 10.1$ g (approx)
Weight of weighing bottle + crystals	$= 11.045$ g
Weight of weighing bottle $\mid$ residual solid	$- 10.155$ g
∴ Weight of crystals used	$= 0.890$ g

This weight of crystals was dissolved in water and made up to 250 cm³ in a graduated flask.

Burette: unknown sodium thiosulphate solution.
Pipette: 25.0 cm³ of potassium iodate solution (3.560 g l⁻¹)
Indicator: starch solution (deep blue → colourless at the end-point).

BURETTE READINGS/cm³		VOLUME OF SODIUM THIOSULPHATE SOLUTION REQUIRED/cm³
Initial	*Final*	
0.15	25.20	25.05 (trial)
0.40	25.30	24.90
0.20	25.15	24.95
0.60	25.55	24.95

Mean volume of sodium thiosulphate required $= 24.93$ cm³.
Molecular weight of $KIO_3 = 39.1 + 126.9 + (3 \times 16.0) = 214.0$

$$\text{Number of moles of } KIO_3 \text{ in } 25.0 \text{ cm}^3 \text{ of solution} = \frac{25.0}{1000} \times \frac{4 \times 0.890}{214}$$

It follows from equations (1) and (2) that 1 mole of IO_3^- liberates a quantity of iodine which reacts with 6 moles of $S_2O_3^{2-}$.

$$\therefore \text{ Number of moles of } S_2O_3^{2-} = 6 \times \frac{25.0}{1000} \times \frac{4 \times 0.890}{214}$$

$$= \frac{24.93}{1000} \times M_{thio} \quad \text{(where } M_{thio} = \text{molar-ity of the sodium thio-sulphate solution)}$$

$$\therefore M_{\text{thio}} = 6 \times \frac{25{\cdot}0}{1000} \times \frac{4 \times 0{\cdot}890}{214} \times \frac{1000}{24{\cdot}93}$$

$$= 0{\cdot}100$$

The sodium thiosulphate solution is 0·100 M.

Alternatively, the calculation could be carried out using the relationship:

$$(MV)_{\text{thio}} = 6(MV)_{\text{iodate}}$$

For further reading

1. E. E. Aynsley and A. B. Littlewood, *Principles of Titrimetric Analysis*. The Royal Institute of Chemistry, 1962.
   A short monograph dealing with the principles of the four types of titration.
2. J. G. Stark, 'The Use of the Molarity Concept in Titrimetric Analysis', *Education in Chemistry*, 1966, 2, 3, 70–76.
3. W. F. Kieffer, *The Mole Concept in Chemistry*, Chapter 6. Chapman and Hall, 1965.
4. G. A. Morrison, 'Volumetric Error', *The School Science Review*, 1966, 162, 47, 506–510.

2 Acid-base Titrations

Acid-base reactions may be considered in terms of the Brönsted-Lowry theory (1923) according to which an *acid* is a substance which can *yield* protons, i.e. it is a proton donor, and a *base* is a substance which can *accept* protons, i.e. it is a proton acceptor.

An acid-base reaction, therefore, involves the transfer of one or more protons from the acid to the base and the stoichiometric equation may be derived using the fact that all protons must be accounted for, i.e. all protons given by the acid must be taken by the base. It should be remembered that the proton is hydrated, i.e. H_3O^+.

Then, for an acid with a basicity b:

$$A \rightarrow bH^+ + \text{products} \qquad (1)$$

and, for a base with an acidity a:

$$B + aH^+ \rightarrow \text{products}. \qquad (2)$$

Equation (1) $\times a$ + equation (2) $\times b$ gives:

$$aA + bB \rightarrow \text{products}.$$

In calculating the equivalent weight of an acid or base by this method it will be seen than 1 gram equivalent of an acid or base in aqueous solution will give or accept one mole* of protons. The equivalent weight of an acid or base is, therefore, its molecular weight divided by the number of protons lost or gained by one molecule of it.

In the reaction of hydrochloric acid with sodium hydroxide, the equation can be written:

$$HCl + NaOH \rightarrow NaCl + H_2O$$

or, ionically,
$$H^+ + OH^- \rightarrow H_2O,$$

so that the reaction involves the transfer of one mole of protons. As 1 mole of NaOH reacts with 1 mole of HCl, it follows that:

$$(MV)_{HCl} = (MV)_{NaOH}$$

In the reaction of sulphuric acid with sodium hydroxide to form the normal sulphate:

$$H_2SO_4 + 2NaOH \rightarrow Na_2SO_4 + 2H_2O$$

or,
$$2H^+ + 2OH^- \rightarrow 2H_2O$$

two moles of protons are transferred from the acid to the base and two moles of NaOH react with one mole of H_2SO_4. Therefore:

$$2(MV)_{acid} = (MV)_{base}$$

The following types of acid-base reactions will be considered, in all of which one or more protons are transferred:

(*a*) reaction of a strong acid with a strong base,

$$H^+ + OH^- \rightarrow H_2O$$

(*b*) reaction of a strong acid with a weak base, e.g. ammonia,

$$H^+ + NH_3 \rightarrow NH_4^+$$

(*c*) reaction of a weak acid, e.g. acetic acid, with a strong base,

$$CH_3COOH + OH^- \rightarrow CH_3COO^- + H_2O$$

(*d*) reaction of a strong acid with a carbonate or hydrogencarbonate,

$$2H^+ + CO_3^{2-} \rightarrow H_2O + CO_2(g)$$
$$H^+ + HCO_3^- \rightarrow H_2O + CO_2(g)$$

The stoichiometric point in these reactions is detected by means of an acid-base indicator. A simplified theory of acid-base indicators has been given in chapter 1 (p. 4): for the detailed theory of indicators and the choice of a suitable indicator for a particular acid-base titration, consult a textbook of physical chemistry (see references at the end of this chapter).

1. Preparation of a standard solution of sodium carbonate

Heat 'Analar' sodium carbonate (approximately 99·9 per cent pure) at about 270 °C for 45–60 minutes to remove the final traces of moisture

* The mole is the *amount of substance* which contains as many atoms, molecules, ions, electrons, etc. as there are atoms in 0·012 kg of carbon-12. Thus, 1 mole of HCl has a mass equal to 36·46 g.

and allow to cool in a desiccator. This process should be carried out in a clean nickel crucible, heated on a sand-bath. The temperature should be checked at intervals and a clean nickel spatula used to stir the contents of the crucible.

Weigh out accurately about 1·3 g of this dry anhydrous sodium carbonate, sealing the weighing bottle during this process to prevent access of water-vapour. Dissolve in water and make up to 250 cm³ of solution in a graduated flask.

Calculate the molarity of the solution (molecular weight of anhydrous $Na_2CO_3 = 106$).

2. Preparation of a standard solution of sulphuric acid

Titrate 25 cm³ aliquot parts of standard sodium carbonate solution (about 0·05 M) with the sulphuric acid, using methyl orange or screened methyl orange as indicator. Bench dilute sulphuric acid (1 M) accurately diluted from 10 cm³ to 250 cm³ is suitable for this titration.

The reaction *with this indicator* is:

$$Na_2CO_3 + H_2SO_4 \rightarrow Na_2SO_4 + H_2O + CO_2(g)$$

or,
$$CO_3^{2-} + 2H^+ \rightarrow CO_2(g) + H_2O$$

∴ 1 mole of carbonate reacts completely with 1 mole of acid and

$$(MV)_{acid} = (MV)_{base}$$

Calculate the molarity and the concentration in g l⁻¹ of the sulphuric acid using

Concentration $= (M_{acid} \times$ molecular weight of sulphuric acid) g l⁻¹.

3. Preparation of a standard solution of sodium hydroxide

Dilute 10 cm³ of bench sodium hydroxide solution (2 M) to 250 cm³ and titrate 25 cm³ aliquot parts with standard sulphuric acid (about 0·05 M), using methyl orange or screened methyl orange as indicator. Calculate the molarity of the sodium hydroxide solution using:

$$(MV)_{base} = 2(MV)_{acid}$$

a relation which follows from the equation for the reaction:

$$H_2SO_4 + 2NaOH \rightarrow Na_2SO_4 + 2H_2O$$

Alternatively, oxalic acid dihydrate, which is obtainable in a highly pure form, may be used as a standard. Weigh out accurately about 1·5 g of the acid and make up to exactly 250 cm³ of solution. Express the concentration as a molarity. Titrate 25 cm³ aliquot parts of the sodium hydroxide solution with the oxalic acid solution, using phenolphthalein as indicator.

Calculate the molarity of the sodium hydroxide solution using:

$$(MV)_{base} = 2(MV)_{acid}$$

a relation which follows from the equation for the reaction:

$$(COOH)_2 + 2NaOH \rightarrow (COONa)_2 + 2H_2O$$

4. Preparation of a standard solution of sodium hydroxide using sulphamic acid

Sulphamic acid, NH_2SO_3H,* is a strong acid obtainable in a pure form. The solid is non-hygroscopic and keeps indefinitely, but an aqueous solution is slowly hydrolysed. It can be titrated with a caustic alkali using either methyl orange or phenolphthalein as indicator:

$$NH_2SO_3^-H^+ + Na^+OH^- \rightarrow NH_2SO_3^-Na^+ + H_2O$$

Sulphamic acid (M.W. 97·1) is a primary standard for acid-base titrations and a standard solution can be prepared by weighing out accurately about 2·5 g of the crystals, dissolving in water and making up to 250 cm³ of solution in a graduated flask.

Calculate the molarity of the solution (it will be approximately 0·1 M).

Titrate 25 cm³ aliquot parts of the sodium hydroxide solution with the sulphamic acid, using methyl orange as indicator. Calculate the molarity of the alkali using:

$$(MV)_{base} = (MV)_{acid}$$

a relation which follows from the equation for the reaction given above.

5. Determination of the percentage of sodium carbonate in washing soda

Weigh out accurately about 4 g of washing soda crystals and make up to exactly 250 cm³ of solution. Titrate 25 cm³ aliquot parts with standard sulphuric acid (about 0·05 M), using methyl orange or screened methyl orange as indicator.

$$CO_3^{2-} + 2H^+ \rightarrow CO_2(g) + H_2O$$

Then, $(MV)_{carb} = (MV)_{acid}$

Calculate the concentration of anhydrous sodium carbonate using:

Concentration $= (M_{carb} \times$ molecular weight of $Na_2CO_3)$ g l⁻¹.

∴ Percentage of sodium carbonate in sample of washing soda

$$= \frac{\text{weight of } Na_2CO_3 \text{ in 1 litre of solution}}{4 \times \text{weight of washing soda crystals used}} \times 100$$

6. Preparation of a standard solution of hydrochloric acid using borax

Recrystallise some 'Analar' borax, hydrated sodium tetraborate $(Na_2B_4O_7.10H_2O)$, from water at a temperature not exceeding 55 °C and

*See references at the end of this chapter.

B

dry by exposure to air overnight. Weigh out accurately about 4·8 g of the borax and make up to exactly 250 cm³ of solution.

Titrate 25 cm³ aliquot parts with hydrochloric acid (10 cm³ of bench acid (2 M) diluted to 250 cm³ is suitable), using methyl red or methyl orange as indicator.

The equation for the reaction is:

$$B_4O_7^{2-} + 2H^+ + 5H_2O \rightarrow 4H_3BO_3$$
$$\therefore (MV)_{acid} = 2(MV)_{borax}$$

Calculate the molarity of the diluted hydrochloric acid.

The boric acid formed in the reaction is a weak acid and so does not affect the titration provided one of the above indicators is used.

7. Determination of the solubility of calcium hydroxide at room temperature

Make a saturated solution of calcium hydroxide and transfer about 75 cm³ (filtered if necessary) to a weighed dry conical flask. Re-weigh. Titrate with standard 0·1 M hydrochloric acid, using methyl orange as indicator.

$$Ca(OH)_2 + 2HCl \rightarrow CaCl_2 + 2H_2O$$
$$\therefore 2(MV)_{ch} = (MV)_{acid}$$

Calculate the number of grams of calcium hydroxide present in the volume of saturated solution used and so the solubility at room temperature in g per 100 g of water.

8. Determination of the percentage of ammonia in an ammonium salt

When an ammonium salt is heated with an excess of sodium hydroxide solution, ammonia is liberated, and the excess alkali may be determined by titration with standard acid:

$$NH_4^+ + OH^- \rightarrow NH_3(g) + H_2O$$

Weigh out accurately about 1·5 g of ammonium sulphate and make up to exactly 250 cm³ of solution. Pipette 25 cm³ of this solution into a conical flask and add exactly 50 cm³ of 0·1 M sodium hydroxide solution. Place a small funnel in the neck of the flask to prevent loss of solution by spray and boil gently until no more ammonia is evolved (test with litmus). Wash the neck of the flask with a small amount of water, cool and titrate the excess of sodium hydroxide with standard hydrochloric acid, using methyl orange as indicator (the acid should be about 0·1 M). Calculate the volume of 0·1 M sodium hydroxide solution required to liberate all the ammonia from the ammonium salt present in 25 cm³ of the solution and hence from the ammonium salt present in 250 cm³ of solution. Then:

Number of moles of NH_3 evolved

$$= \frac{0{\cdot}1 \times \text{volume of NaOH required}}{1000} \text{ (see equation on p. 14)}$$

Hence, calculate the weight of ammonia evolved and the percentage of ammonia in the salt.

9. Determination of the percentage purity of a nitrate

Weigh out accurately about 0·25 g of potassium nitrate and transfer it to a conical flask. Add about 2 g of Devarda's alloy, which contains about 45 per cent aluminium, and 50 cm³ of dilute sodium hydroxide solution. Set up the apparatus as shown in Fig. 2.1. Heat the mixture in the reaction flask gently and distil all the ammonia into the receiver containing

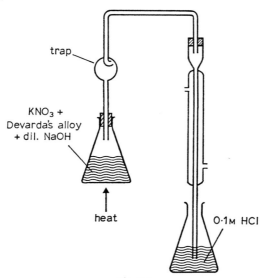

trap

KNO₃ +
Devarda's alloy
+ dil. NaOH

heat

0·1M HCl

Fig. 2.1

exactly 50 cm³ of 0·1 M hydrochloric acid, taking care to avoid sucking back of the acid into the condenser. Boil gently for 20 minutes or until the reduction of the nitrate to ammonia is complete:

$$3NO_3^- + 8Al + 5OH^- + 18H_2O \rightarrow 8Al(OH)_4^- + 3NH_3(g)$$

Wash the inside of the condenser thoroughly and collect the washings in the receiver. Titrate the contents of the receiver and washings with standard 0·1 M sodium hydroxide solution and methyl red as indicator.

Calculate the volume and hence the number of moles of HCl neutralised by the ammonia evolved. From this, calculate the amount of potassium nitrate in the sample and its percentage purity.

10. Titration of orthophosphoric acid

When orthophosphoric acid is titrated with sodium hydroxide, the following reactions occur:

$$H_3PO_4 + OH^- \rightarrow H_2PO_4^- + H_2O \tag{1}$$
$$H_2PO_4^- + OH^- \rightarrow HPO_4^{2-} + H_2O \tag{2}$$
$$HPO_4^{2-} + OH^- \rightarrow PO_4^{3-} + H_2O \tag{3}$$

Methyl orange changes colour when reaction (1) is complete, i.e. the acid has been converted to its sodium dihydrogen salt, while phenolphthalein changes colour when reaction (2) is complete, i.e. the acid has been converted to its disodium salt. No indicator is satisfactory for reaction (3), as the solution of the trisodium salt is strongly alkaline by hydrolysis (see Fig. 2.2).

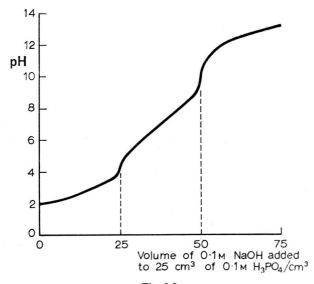

Fig. 2.2

Weigh out accurately about 2·5 g of syrupy (90 per cent) phosphoric acid and make up to exactly 250 cm³ of solution. Titrate 25 cm³ aliquot parts with standard 0·2 M sodium hydroxide using (a) methyl orange and (b) phenolphthalein, as indicators.

It will be found that the volumes of sodium hydroxide required in the two titrations are in the ratio of 1 : 2.

For reaction (1): $(MV)_{acid} = (MV)_{base}$
For reaction (2): $2(MV)_{acid} = (MV)_{base}$

Use the titration results to prepare crystals of the sodium dihydrogen, disodium and trisodium salts of orthophosphoric acid.

11. Determination of the amounts of sodium hydroxide and sodium carbonate in a mixed solution

(a) Titrate 25 cm³ aliquot parts of the given solution (a mixture of about 2·5 g of anhydrous sodium carbonate and 2·0 g of sodium hydroxide made up to 1 litre of solution is suitable) with 0·1 M hydrochloric acid, using phenolphthalein as indicator. At the end-point, i.e. when the colour of the indicator has changed from pink to colourless, the reactions which have occurred are:

$$OH^- + H^+ \rightarrow H_2O \tag{1}$$
and
$$CO_3^{2-} + H^+ \rightarrow HCO_3^- \tag{2}$$

Now add methyl orange to this colourless solution and add more hydrochloric acid until the end-point is reached, i.e. the colour of the indicator changes from yellow to orange. The further reaction which has now taken place is:

$$HCO_3^- + H^+ \rightarrow H_2O + CO_2(g) \tag{3}$$

The titration with phenolphthalein represents the complete neutralisation of the sodium hydroxide (1) and the half-neutralisation of the sodium carbonate (2). The titration with methyl orange represents the half-neutralisation of the carbonate (3).

As one mole of hydroxide reacts with one mole of acid in equation (1) and one mole of carbonate reacts with one mole of acid in equation (2), it follows that:

$(MV)_{NaOH} + (MV)_{carb} = (MV)_{acid}$ (where $V_{NaOH} = V_{carb}$ = volume of mixture, and V_{acid} = volume of acid using phenolphthalein).

The molarity of the hydrogencarbonate is given by:

$(MV)_{carb} = (MV')_{acid}$ (where V'_{acid} = additional volume of acid using methyl orange

and V_{carb} = volume of mixture)

$$\therefore \qquad (MV)_{NaOH} = (MV)_{acid} - (MV')_{acid}$$

The concentrations may then be obtained from:

Concentration of $Na_2CO_3 = (M_{carb} \times$ molecular weight of Na_2CO_3) g l^{-1}

and, concentration of NaOH $= (M_{NaOH} \times$ molecular weight of NaOH) g l^{-1}.

(b) An alternative method involves the precipitation of the carbonate by addition of barium chloride solution:

$$Ba^{2+} + CO_3^{2-} \rightarrow BaCO_3(s)$$

First determine the total molarity by titrating 25 cm³ aliquot parts of the solution with standard hydrochloric acid (about 0·1 M), using methyl orange as indicator.

Now transfer 25 cm³ aliquot parts of the solution to a conical flask, add an excess of neutral barium chloride solution and titrate with standard hydrochloric acid, using phenolphthalein as indicator. The titration should be carried out slowly and with constant stirring.

The total molarity is given by:

$(MV)_{NaOH} + 2(MV)_{carb} = (MV)_{acid}$ (where $V_{NaOH} = V_{carb}$ = volume of mixture, and V_{acid} = volume of acid in first titration)

and the molarity of the NaOH is given by:

$(MV)_{NaOH} = (MV')_{acid}$ (where V'_{acid} = volume of acid in second titration and V_{NaOH} = volume of mixture).

The concentration may then be calculated as in method (a).

12. Determination of the concentration of a given solution of barium chloride

The barium ions are precipitated by addition of an excess of sodium carbonate in neutral or alkaline solution:

$$Ba^{2+} + CO_3^{2-} \rightarrow BaCO_3(s) \tag{1}$$

and the white precipitate of barium carbonate is filtered off and the excess of carbonate determined by titration with standard acid.

Transfer 25 cm³ aliquot parts of the barium chloride solution (about 0·1 M) to a beaker, boil and add exactly 50 cm³ of standard sodium carbonate solution (about 0·1 M). Filter the mixture into a conical flask, wash the beaker and precipitate with water several times and collect the washings with the filtrate. Determine the excess of sodium carbonate in the total filtrate by titration with standard 0·1 M hydrochloric acid, using methyl orange as indicator.

Calculate the volume of sodium carbonate solution required to react with the barium chloride according to equation (1) and hence the molarity of the barium chloride using:

$$(MV)_{BaCl_2} = (MV)_{carb}$$

Then, concentration of barium chloride = (M_{BaCl_2} × molecular weight of barium chloride) g l⁻¹.

Worked example

5·35 g of an ammonium salt were dissolved in water and the solution was diluted to 1 litre. 25·0 cm³ of this solution were boiled with 50·0 cm³ of 0·1 M sodium hydroxide solution until no more ammonia was evolved. The excess of sodium hydroxide then required 25·0 cm³ of 0·1 M hydrochloric acid for neutralisation. Calculate the percentage of ammonia in the ammonium salt.

The equations for the reactions are

$$NH_4^+ + OH^- \rightarrow NH_3(g) + H_2O \tag{1}$$

and,

$$H^+ + OH^- \rightarrow H_2O \tag{2}$$

$\therefore$ 25·0 cm³ of 0·1 M HCl react with 25·0 cm³ of 0·1 M NaOH (from equation (2)) and the volume of 0·1 M NaOH solution reacting with the NH_3 evolved

$$= (50·0 - 25·0) = 25·0 \text{ cm}^3$$

$\therefore$ Number of moles of NH_3 evolved $= \dfrac{25·0}{1000} \times 0·1$ (from equation (1))

and, weight of NH_3 evolved $= \dfrac{25·0}{1000} \times 0·1 \times 17$

$$= 0·0425 \text{ g}$$

But, 25·0 cm³ of solution contain $5·35 \times \dfrac{25·0}{1000}$

$$= 0·134 \text{ g of the ammonium salt}$$

$\therefore$ Percentage of NH_3 in the ammonium salt $= \dfrac{0·0425}{0·134} \times 100$

$$= 31·7.$$

Additional Problems

1. A is a solution containing 8·0 g of the salt $Na_2CO_3.xNaHCO_3.yH_2O$ per litre.

(a) Titrate 25 cm³ aliquot parts of A with standard hydrochloric acid (about 0·1 M) using (i) phenolphthalein, (ii) methyl orange as indicator in separate titrations.

From the ratio of the volumes of acid required with the two indicators, calculate the number of molecules of sodium hydrogencarbonate (x) associated with one molecule of sodium carbonate in the salt.

(b) Heat about 2 g of the salt (weighed accurately) to constant weight at 250 °C, when the water of crystallisation is evolved as water vapour and the hydrogencarbonate decomposes to carbonate.

From the loss in weight, calculate the number of molecules of water of crystallisation (y) in one molecule of the salt.

2. Solution B contains 120 g of the salt $NaNH_4HPO_4.xH_2O$ per litre.

(a) Transfer 25 cm³ aliquot parts of solution B to a conical flask and add an equal volume of 1 M sodium hydroxide solution. Boil the mixture gently for several minutes, taking care to avoid loss by spray, until ammonia is no longer detectable in the steam above the liquid (test with litmus). Allow the solution to cool thoroughly and titrate it with standard hydrochloric acid (about 1 M), using phenolphthalein as indicator.

(b) Calculate:
(i) the weight of ammonia driven off by the action of the sodium hydroxide solution, using the equation:

$$NaNH_4HPO_4 + NaOH \rightarrow Na_2HPO_4 + NH_3(g) + H_2O,$$

(*ii*) the value of x.

3. Mercury(II) oxide dissolves in potassium bromide solution with the formation of the complex tetrabromomercurate(II) ion, $[HgBr_4]^{2-}$, and potassium hydroxide:

$$HgO + 4Br^- + H_2O \rightarrow [HgBr_4]^{2-} + 2OH^-$$

Use this reaction to prepare a standard solution of potassium hydroxide (approximately 0·1 M) and check its molarity by titration with an acid of known molarity using methyl orange or phenolphthalein as indicator.

Note. 'Analar' mercury(II) oxide should be used for this purpose, together with an excess of 'Analar' potassium bromide.

4. Formaldehyde reacts with a solution of an ammonium salt to give a solution which behaves as a strong acid, together with a weak base, hexamethylenetetramine, $(CH_2)_6N_4$. The solution can be titrated with standard alkali using phenolphthalein as indicator, as the hexamethylenetetramine does not interfere.

Investigate the stoichiometry of the reaction as follows:

(*a*) Dilute 40 per cent formaldehyde solution ('formalin')* approximately 100 times and pipette 25 cm³ of the diluted solution (approximately 0·4 per cent) into a conical flask. Add 50 cm³ of exactly 0·1 M iodine solution, followed by 1 M sodium hydroxide solution until the solution is pale yellow. The sodium hydroxide should be added slowly with thorough mixing. Allow the solution to stand for 5 minutes, then acidify with dilute hydrochloric acid and titrate the excess of iodine with standard 0·1 M sodium thiosulphate solution (see page 37). Calculate the molarity of the formaldehyde solution, using the equation:

$$H.CHO + I_2 + 3OH^- \rightarrow H.COO^- + 2I^- + 2H_2O$$

(*b*) Transfer 25 cm³ aliquot parts of 1 M ammonium chloride solution (an excess) to a conical flask, add an equal volume of the standard formaldehyde solution (previously neutralised to phenolphthalein) and heat the mixture for 5 minutes. Allow to cool and titrate with standard 0·1 M sodium hydroxide solution using phenolphthalein as indicator.

(*c*) Calculate the molar ratio of formaldehyde to ammonium chloride and hence write an equation for the reaction.

For further reading

1. L. C. Roselaar, *Systematic Physical Chemistry*, pp. 156–158 and 162–165. John Murray, 1975.
   pH changes during acid-base titrations and the theory of acid-base indicators.
2. E. E. Aynsley and A. B. Littlewood, *Principles of Titrimetric Analysis*, pp. 15–22 and 37–40. The Royal Institute of Chemistry, 1962.

*If the formalin contains a white solid polymer it should be refluxed until a clear solution is obtained.

3. A. I. Vogel, *A Textbook of Quantitative Inorganic Analysis* (Third Edition), pp. 51–72. Longmans, 1962.
The theory of acid-base titrations.
4. D. Nicholls, *Modern Chemistry*, pp. 191–204. Penguin Books, 1970.
A clear discussion of the main theories of acids and bases.
5. J. G. Stark, 'Sulphamic Acid', *The School Science Review,* 1965, 161, **47**, 169–172.
6. J. Waser, 'Acid-Base Titration and Distribution Curves', *Journal of Chemical Education,* 1967, 5, **44**, 274–276.

3 Redox Titrations

Oxidation-reduction (or *redox*) reactions may be considered in terms of the electron transfer theory according to which *oxidation* is a process involving the *loss of electrons* from a reducing agent, i.e. an increase in the oxidation number* of an element, and *reduction* is a process involving the *gain of electrons* by an oxidising agent, i.e. a decrease in the oxidation number of an element.

A redox reaction can, therefore, be divided into two parts: in one half the reducing agent *loses* electrons and in the other half the oxidising agent *gains* electrons. The stoichiometric equation for a redox reaction may then be derived using the fact that all the electrons lost by the reducing agent must be gained by the oxidising agent. For example, the half-reactions for a reducing agent A and an oxidising agent B may be written as follows:

$$A - be^- \rightarrow \text{products} \quad (oxidation) \quad (1)$$
$$B + ae^- \rightarrow \text{products} \quad (reduction) \quad (2)$$

Equation (1) $\times a +$ equation (2) $\times b$ gives:

$$aA + bB \rightarrow \text{products.}$$

The equation for the oxidation of iron(II) ions by permanganate ions in sulphuric acid solution may then be derived as follows:

$$Fe^{2+} - e^- \rightarrow Fe^{3+}, \quad \text{i.e. Fe(II)} \rightarrow \text{Fe(III)} \ (oxidation) \ (3)$$
$$MnO_4^- + 8H^+ + 5e^- \rightarrow Mn^{2+} + 4H_2O,$$
$$\text{i.e. Mn(VII)} \rightarrow \text{Mn(II)} \quad (reduction) \quad (4)$$

Equation (3) $\times 5 +$ equation (4) gives:

$$MnO_4^- + 5Fe^{2+} + 8H^+ \rightarrow Mn^{2+} + 5Fe^{3+} + 4H_2O \quad (5)$$

*See references at the end of this chapter.

The half-reaction for a given reducing or oxidising agent reacting in a particular way is always the same, irrespective of the particular overall reaction, e.g. for all oxidation reactions by permanganate ions in sulphuric acid solution the equation for the half-reaction is:

$$MnO_4^- + 8H^+ + 5e^- \rightarrow Mn^{2+} + 4H_2O \tag{4}$$

In calculating the equivalent weight of a reducing or oxidising agent by this method it will be seen that the oxidation of iron(II) to iron(III) (equation (3)) involves the loss of one electron from the iron(II) with a corresponding increase in oxidation number of $+2$ to $+3$, and the reduction of manganese(VII) to manganese(II) (equation (4)) involves the gain of five electrons by the manganese(VII) with a corresponding decrease in oxidation number from $+7$ to $+2$. Therefore, *in this reaction*, the equivalent weight of an iron(II) salt is equal to its molecular weight and the equivalent weight of the permanganate is equal to one-fifth of its molecular weight. In general, the equivalent weight of a reducing or oxidising agent is its molecular weight divided by the number of electrons lost or gained by one molecule of it, *in the relevant reaction*.

Redox and acid-base reactions are similar in that the essential processes involved are electron transfer and proton transfer respectively. However, they differ in one important respect—electron transfer is accompanied by a change in oxidation number while proton transfer is not, e.g.

$$H_2S + 2OH^- \rightarrow 2H_2O + S^{2-},$$
$$\text{i.e. } S\,(-2) \rightarrow S\,(-2) \quad \textit{(acid-base)}$$
$$H_2S\,(aq) - 2e^- \rightarrow 2H^+\,(aq) + S,$$
$$\text{i.e. } S\,(-2) \rightarrow S\,(0) \quad \textit{(redox)}$$

The end-point in a redox titration may be detected by means of the change in colour of one of the reagents, e.g. potassium permanganate, or by the use of a redox indicator, e.g. barium diphenylamine *p*-sulphonate, which changes colour as soon as the oxidising agent is in an excess of the amount required for completion of the reaction.

Some common reagents used in redox titrations are listed below.

(*a*) **Potassium permanganate**, $KMnO_4$, an oxidising agent which is purple in colour but effectively colourless in the reduced form (Mn^{2+}). It is, therefore, used as a self-indicator. In *acid* solution:

$$MnO_4^- + 8H^+ + 5e^- \rightarrow Mn^{2+} + 4H_2O$$

Molecular weight $= 158 \cdot 0$ and equivalent weight $= \dfrac{\text{M.W.}}{5} = 31 \cdot 6.$

Note. In neutral and alkaline solution the reaction follows a different course and different numbers of electrons are required.

It will oxidise:

(*i*) iron(II) to iron(III),

$Fe^{2+} - e^- \rightarrow Fe^{3+}$ (equivalent weight of iron(II) salt $=$ M.W.)

(*ii*) oxalates to carbon dioxide (at 80 °C, as the reaction is too slow at room temperature),

$$\begin{array}{c} COO^- \\ | \\ COO^- \end{array} - 2e^- \rightarrow 2CO_2(g) \left(\text{equivalent weight of oxalate} = \frac{M.W.}{2} \right)$$

(*iii*) hydrogen peroxide to oxygen,

$$H_2O_2 - 2e^- \rightarrow 2H^+ + O_2(g)$$

(molecular weight $= 34\cdot0$ and equivalent weight $= \dfrac{M.W.}{2} = 17\cdot0$).

Potassium permanganate cannot be used with solutions containing hydrochloric acid, which it oxidises to chlorine, or in the presence of nitric acid, which is itself an oxidising agent. It is, therefore, normally acidified with dilute sulphuric acid.

(*b*) **Potassium dichromate**, $K_2Cr_2O_7$, an oxidising agent which is orange in colour but green in the reduced form (hydrated Cr^{3+}). Barium diphenylamine *p*-sulphonate is used as indicator, being violet in the presence of an excess of dichromate ions. In *acid* solution:

$$Cr_2O_7^{2-} + 14H^+ + 6e^- \rightarrow 2Cr^{3+} + 7H_2O, \quad \text{i.e. } Cr(VI) \rightarrow Cr(III)$$

(molecular weight $= 294\cdot2$ and equivalent weight $= \dfrac{M.W.}{6} = 49\cdot0$).

It will oxidise:
(*i*) iron(II) to iron(III), as for potassium permanganate, but it can be used in the presence of hydrochloric acid,*

$$Fe^{2+} - e^- \rightarrow Fe^{3+}$$

(*ii*) iodide ion to iodine,

$$2I^- - 2e^- \rightarrow I_2$$

(*c*) **Iodine**, I_2, an oxidising agent which has a red-brown colour when dissolved in aqueous potassium iodide,

$$I_2 + I^- \rightleftharpoons I_3^-$$

but is colourless in the reduced form (I^-),

$$I_2 + 2e^- \rightarrow 2I^-, \quad \text{i.e. } I(0) \rightarrow I(-1)$$

(molecular weight $= 253\cdot8$ and equivalent weight $= \dfrac{M.W.}{2} = 126\cdot9$).

It will oxidise:
(*i*) arsenic(III) oxide and arsenites,

$$As_2O_3 + 2H_2O - 4e^- \rightleftharpoons As_2O_5 + 4H^+$$

(this reaction is reversible, but it is quantitative in the presence of the basic HCO_3^- ion).

*See table of redox potentials in Appendix II.

(molecular weight of As_2O_3 = 197·8 and equivalent weight =

$$\frac{M.W.}{4} = 49·4).$$

(ii) sodium thiosulphate to sodium tetrathionate,

$$2S_2O_3{}^{2-} - 2e^- \to S_4O_6{}^{2-}$$

(molecular weight = 248·2 and equivalent weight = M.W.)

Iodine solutions are sometimes used directly in titrimetric analysis, but more frequently iodine is an intermediate, being liberated quantitatively from an excess of acidified iodide by an oxidising agent. The iodine is then quantitatively reduced to iodide again by titration with sodium thiosulphate.

(d) **Sodium thiosulphate**, $Na_2S_2O_3.5H_2O$, a reducing agent which is colourless. It is colourless also in the oxidised form ($S_4O_6{}^{2-}$). It is used for the determination of iodine and of oxidising agents which liberate iodine from acidified iodide. Starch is used as indicator, giving a deep blue colour in the presence of iodine.

$$2S_2O_3{}^{2-} - 2e^- \to S_4O_6{}^{2-}$$

(molecular weight = 248·2 and equivalent weight = M.W.)

The oxidation number of the sulphur increases from +2 in the thiosulphate to $+2\frac{1}{2}$ in the tetrathionate.

Potassium permanganate, $KMnO_4$

Preparation

Fuse 1 g of potassium chlorate and 2·5 g of potassium hydroxide together in a crucible. Add carefully to the molten mass 2 g of manganese dioxide a little at a time, increasing the temperature so as to keep the mixture molten:

$$ClO_3{}^- + 6OH^- + 3MnO_2 \to Cl^- + 3MnO_4{}^{2-} + 3H_2O,$$
$$\text{i.e. } Mn(IV) \to Mn(VI)$$

Cool the green mass of potassium manganate, powder it in a mortar and dissolve it in about 40 cm³ of water. Filter through glass wool, boil the filtrate and pass carbon dioxide through it until there is no trace of the green manganate left (this can be checked by placing one drop of the mixture on a filter paper):

$$3MnO_4{}^{2-} + 2H_2O + 4CO_2 \rightleftharpoons 2MnO_4{}^- + MnO_2(s) + 4HCO_3{}^-$$

Filter immediately, evaporate the purple filtrate to one-third volume and allow to crystallise. The product may be recrystallised from the minimum volume of nearly-boiling water, when the crystals should be filtered off on a Hirsch funnel and dried in an oven.

Note. Disproportionation occurs on addition of the carbon dioxide:

$$3Mn(VI) \to 2Mn(VII) + Mn(IV)$$

and one-third of the manganese is precipitated as the dioxide.

Reactions
  1. Dissolve some of the crystals in water and add dilute sulphuric acid
to separate portions, followed by:
   (*a*) potassium iodide solution,
   (*b*) ammonium iron(II) sulphate solution,
   (*c*) a few crystals of oxalic acid, then warm,
   (*d*) 20-volume hydrogen peroxide solution,
   (*e*) concentrated hydrochloric acid.
  2. Repeat (*a*) above in alkaline solution, e.g. in the presence of sodium
carbonate.
  3. Heat a few crystals strongly, testing any gas evolved. Cool, add
water and note any visible change.

TITRATIONS USING POTASSIUM PERMANGANATE

**1. Preparation of a standard solution of potassium permanganate using
sodium oxalate**

Potassium permanganate slowly decomposes in solution, especially in
sunlight, and readily oxidises organic matter. It cannot, therefore, be
used directly as a standard reagent in titrimetric analysis. An approximately 0·02 M solution can be made by dissolving 3·2 g of 'Analar'
potassium permanganate in hot water* and making up to 1 litre of
solution. The exact molarity can then be found using 'Analar' sodium
oxalate, $Na_2C_2O_4$, which can be dried in an oven and allowed to cool
in a desiccator before use.
   Weigh out accurately about 1·5 g of 'Analar' sodium oxalate,
$Na_2C_2O_4$, and make up to exactly 250 cm³ of solution. This solution
will be about 0·05 M. Pipette 25 cm³ of this solution† into a conical
flask, add about 25 cm³ of dilute sulphuric acid and heat the contents
of the flask to approximately 80 °C. Titrate with the approximately
0·02 M permanganate solution until a permanent pink colour is obtained. The pink colour may not be immediately discharged in the
initial stages of the titration as the reaction is slow until sufficient Mn^{2+}
ions have been produced to catalyse the reaction ('autocatalysis'). The
mixture in the flask must be thoroughly shaken during the titration and,
if the temperature falls appreciably, further heating will be necessary.
Calculate the molarity of the permanganate solution using:

$$5(MV)_{perm} = 2(MV)_{oxal}$$

a relation which follows from the equation for the reaction:

$$\begin{matrix} COO^- \\ | \\ COO^- \end{matrix} - 2e^- \rightarrow 2CO_2(g) \qquad (6)$$

*The solution should be filtered through glass wool if necessary.
†This must be done with care as oxalates are poisonous.

$$MnO_4^- + 8H^+ + 5e^- \rightarrow Mn^{2+} + 4H_2O \qquad (4)$$

giving,

$$2MnO_4^- + 5 \begin{array}{c} COO^- \\ | \\ COO^- \end{array} + 16H^+ \rightarrow 2Mn^{2+} + 10CO_2(g) + 8H_2O \qquad (7)$$

2. Preparation of a standard solution of potassium permanganate using arsenic(III) oxide

Arsenic(III) oxide, As_2O_3, is not very soluble in water, but dissolves readily in sodium hydroxide solution to form sodium arsenite. The arsenious acid, formed by acidification of this solution, may then be oxidised by potassium permanganate to arsenic acid:

$$5H_3AsO_3 + 2MnO_4^- + 6H^+ \rightarrow 5H_3AsO_4 + 2Mn^{2+} + 3H_2O \qquad (8)$$

What are the equations for the corresponding half-reactions?

Weigh out accurately about 1·25 g of arsenic(III) oxide, previously dried in an oven and allowed to cool in a desiccator, and dissolve in sodium hydroxide solution. Transfer this solution quantitatively to a 250 cm³ graduated flask and make up to the mark. Measure out 25 cm³ of this solution into a conical flask *using a burette.* Add a few drops of phenolphthalein, dilute hydrochloric acid until the indicator is just decolorised and then one drop of 0·0025 M potassium iodide solution (0·41 g of KI per litre) as a catalyst. Titrate with the approximately 0·02 M permanganate solution, going very slowly near the end-point when more permanganate should be added only when the previous drop has been decolorised. Calculate the molarity of the permanganate solution using:

$$5(MV)_{perm} = 4(MV)_{As_2O_3}$$

a relation which follows from the equation for the reaction (8).

Note. One molecule of As_2O_3 contains *two* atoms of arsenic.

3. Determination of the number of molecules of water of crystallisation in ammonium iron(II) sulphate crystals

Weigh out accurately about 9·8 g of ammonium iron(II) sulphate crystals, dissolve in cold water, add about 25 cm³ of dilute sulphuric acid and make up to exactly 250 cm³ of solution. This solution will be about 0·1 M. As ammonium iron(II) sulphate is a double salt, the properties of its solution will be those of its component ions. The actual reducing agent is, therefore, the iron(II) ion:

$$Fe^{2+} - e^- \rightarrow Fe^{3+} \qquad (3)$$

so that the overall equation for the reaction is:

$$MnO_4^- + 5Fe^{2+} + 8H^+ \rightarrow Mn^{2+} + 5Fe^{3+} + 4H_2O \qquad (5)$$

Pipette 25 cm³ of this ammonium iron(II) sulphate solution into a conical flask and add about 25 cm³ of dilute sulphuric acid. Titrate with standard potassium permanganate solution (about 0·02 M) in the burette until a permanent pink colour is obtained. Calculate the molarity of the ammonium iron(II) sulphate solution from first principles or by using the relation:

$$(MV)_{Fe^{2+}} = 5(MV)_{perm} \quad \text{(see equation (5))}$$

Then, molecular weight of hydrated ammonium iron(II) sulphate

$$= \frac{4 \times \text{weight of crystals used}}{M_{Fe^{2+}}}$$

= molecular weight of anhydrous double salt (284) + 18n

from which n, the number of molecules of water of crystallisation, can be calculated.

4. Determination of the percentage of iron in iron wire

Weigh out accurately about 1·4 g of iron wire and transfer it to a conical flask containing 25 cm³ of dilute sulphuric acid and a few cm³ of concentrated sulphuric acid to accelerate the reaction. Fit the flask with a rubber bung containing a short length of capillary tubing which allows the hydrogen produced to escape but effectively prevents the entry of air, so that no oxidation of iron(II) can occur:

$$\text{Fe} + 2H^+ \rightarrow Fe^{2+} + H_2(g)$$

Warm the flask carefully to maintain a steady reaction and, when all the iron has reacted leaving only particles of carbon, cool the flask. Transfer the solution quantitatively to a 250 cm³ graduated flask and make up to the mark with dilute sulphuric acid and water. Pipette 25 cm³ of this solution into a conical flask, add about 25 cm³ of dilute sulphuric acid and titrate with standard potassium permanganate solution (about 0·02 M).

Calculate the molarity of the iron(II) solution using:

$$(MV)_{Fe^{2+}} = 5(MV)_{perm} \quad \text{(see equation (5))}$$

Then, concentration of Fe^{2+} ions = ($M_{Fe^{2+}} \times$ atomic weight of iron) g l^{-1}.

∴ Percentage of iron in iron wire

$$= \frac{\text{weight of iron in 1 litre of solution}}{4 \times \text{weight of iron wire used}} \times 100$$

5. Determination of the percentage of iron in ammonium iron(III) alum

The iron(III) ions present in the alum must first be reduced to iron(II) and this is then titrated with standard potassium permanganate solution. The reduction may be carried out rapidly using zinc amalgam.

Weigh out accurately about 12 g of the alum $NH_4Fe(SO_4)_2.12H_2O$, add 25 cm^3 of dilute sulphuric acid and make up to exactly 250 cm^3 of solution. Pipette 25 cm^3 of this solution into a reagent bottle containing zinc amalgam.* Stopper the bottle securely and shake vigorously for a few minutes until, on withdrawing one drop on a glass rod, no colour is obtained with potassium thiocyanate:

$$Fe^{3+} + e^- \rightarrow Fe^{2+} \tag{9}$$

Pour as much as possible of the aqueous solution into a conical flask and wash the amalgam several times with water, adding the washings to the flask. Add about 25 cm^3 of dilute sulphuric acid and titrate the solution and washings with standard potassium permanganate solution (about 0·02 M).

Calculate the molarity of the Fe^{3+} ions using:

$$(MV)_{Fe^{3+}} = 5(MV)_{perm} \quad \text{(see equations (5) and (9))}$$

Then, concentration of Fe^{3+} ions $= (M_{Fe^{3+}} \times \text{atomic weight of iron}) \, g \, l^{-1}$.

∴ Percentage of iron in the alum

$$= \frac{\text{weight of iron in 1 litre of solution}}{4 \times \text{weight of alum used}} \times 100$$

6. Determination of the number of molecules of water of crystallisation in oxalic acid crystals

Weigh out accurately about 1·5 g of oxalic acid crystals and make up to exactly 250 cm^3 of solution. Pipette 25 cm^3 of this solution into a conical flask (care!), add about 25 cm^3 of dilute sulphuric acid, heat to approximately 80 °C and titrate the hot solution with standard potassium permanganate solution (about 0·02 M).

Calculate the molarity of the oxalic acid solution using:

$$2(MV)_{oxal} = 5(MV)_{perm} \quad \text{(see equation (7))}$$

Then, molecular weight of hydrated oxalic acid

$$= \frac{4 \times \text{weight of crystals used}}{M_{oxal}}$$

$$= \text{molecular weight of anhydrous acid (90·0)} + 18n$$

from which n, the number of molecules of water of crystallisation, can be calculated.

7. Determination of the volume concentration of hydrogen peroxide

Hydrogen peroxide is itself an oxidising agent, being reduced to water in the process. However, it can also act as a reducing agent (see redox

*See Appendix II.

potentials), e.g. with potassium permanganate, when it is oxidised to oxygen. The equation for its reaction with permanganate ions in sulphuric acid solution may be derived by means of the equations for the half-reactions:

$$H_2O_2 - 2e^- \rightarrow O_2(g) + 2H^+, \quad i.e. \ O(-1) \rightarrow O(0) \ (oxidation) \quad (10)$$
$$MnO_4^- + 8H^+ + 5e^- \rightarrow Mn^{2+} + 4H_2O \quad (4)$$

Equation (10) × 5 + equation (4) × 2 gives:

$$2MnO_4^- + 5H_2O_2 + 6H^+ \rightarrow 2Mn^{2+} + 5O_2(g) + 8H_2O \quad (11)$$

Dilute 5 cm³ of nominal 20-volume hydrogen peroxide solution accurately to 250 cm³ in a graduated flask and mix thoroughly. Titrate 25 cm³ aliquot parts of the diluted solution, acidified with about 25 cm³ of dilute sulphuric acid, with standard potassium permanganate solution (about 0·02 M).

Calculate the molarity of the diluted solution using:

$$2(MV)_{H_2O_2(dil)} = 5(MV)_{perm} \quad \text{(see equation (11))}$$

and hence the molarity of the original hydrogen peroxide solution ($M_{H_2O_2}$). Then, concentration of hydrogen peroxide solution

$$= (M_{H_2O_2} \times \text{molecular weight of hydrogen peroxide}) \ g \ l^{-1}.$$

The volume concentration is the volume of oxygen available from unit volume of the hydrogen peroxide solution measured at s.t.p.

$$2H_2O_2 \rightarrow 2H_2O + O_2(g)$$
$$68 \ g \qquad 22{\cdot}4 \ l \ \text{at s.t.p.}$$

∴ By definition a 22·4-volume solution contains 68 g l⁻¹.
Hence calculate the volume concentration of the original hydrogen peroxide solution.

Worked example

25·0 cm³ of a solution of hydrogen peroxide, acidified with dilute sulphuric acid, required 44·6 cm³ of 0·02 M potassium permanganate solution for complete reaction. Calculate the volume concentration of the hydrogen peroxide solution.

The equations for the half reactions are

$$H_2O_2 - 2e^- \rightarrow O_2(g) + 2H^+$$

and,
$$MnO_4^- + 8H^+ + 5e^- \rightarrow Mn^{2+} + 4H_2O$$

giving the following equation for the overall reaction:

$$2MnO_4^- + 5H_2O_2 + 6H^+ \rightarrow 2Mn^{2+} + 5O_2(g) + 8H_2O \quad (11)$$

Number of moles of MnO_4^- reacting $= \dfrac{44{\cdot}6}{1000} \times 0{\cdot}02$

c

$$\therefore \text{ Number of moles of } H_2O_2 = \frac{5}{2} \times \frac{44 \cdot 6}{1000} \times 0 \cdot 02 \quad \text{(from equation (11))}$$

$$= \frac{25 \cdot 0}{1000} \times M_{H_2O_2}$$

$$\therefore M_{H_2O_2} = \frac{5}{2} \times \frac{44 \cdot 6}{1000} \times 0 \cdot 02 \times \frac{1000}{25 \cdot 0}$$

$$= 0 \cdot 0892$$

and concentration of $H_2O_2 = 0 \cdot 0892 \times 34 = 3 \cdot 03 \text{ g l}^{-1}$

$$2H_2O_2 \rightarrow 2H_2O + O_2(g)$$
$$68 \text{ g} \qquad 22 \cdot 4 \text{ l at s.t.p.}$$

$\therefore$ A solution containing 68 g of H_2O_2 per $1 = 22 \cdot 4$ volumes and a

solution containing $3 \cdot 03 \text{ g l}^{-1} = \dfrac{3 \cdot 03}{68} \times 22 \cdot 4 = 1 \cdot 0$ volume.

Additional Problems

1. Weigh out accurately about 2 g of pure potassium tetroxalate and make it up to exactly 250 cm³ of solution.

(a) Titrate 25 cm³ aliquot parts of this solution with standard sodium hydroxide solution (about 0·1 M), using phenolphthalein as indicator.

(b) Heat 25 cm³ aliquot parts of the solution, acidified with about 25 cm³ of dilute sulphuric acid, to approximately 80 °C and titrate with standard potassium permanganate solution (about 0·02 M).

(c) From the results in (a) and (b) calculate:

    (i) the concentration of hydrogen ion in the solution in mol l^{-1},

    (ii) the concentration of oxalate ion in the solution in mol l^{-1},

    (iii) the numerical values of x, y and z in the formula xKHC$_2$O$_4$. yH$_2$C$_2$O$_4$.zH$_2$O for the oxalate, assuming that the values of x, y and z are small whole numbers.

2. Weigh out accurately about 1·5 g of pure iron(II) oxalate, dissolve it in dilute sulphuric acid and make up to exactly 250 cm³ of solution.

Heat 25 cm³ aliquot parts of this solution, acidified with about 25 cm³ of dilute sulphuric acid, to approximately 80 °C and titrate the hot solution with standard potassium permanganate solution (about 0·02 M).

Calculate the molar ratio of iron(II) oxalate, FeC_2O_4, to MnO_4^- and hence derive an equation for the oxidation of iron(II) oxalate by permanganate ion in sulphuric acid solution.

3. Determine the percentage of calcium in a sample of calcium carbonate (preferably 'Analar') by the following method.

Dissolve an accurately known weight (about 0·15 g) of the sample in dilute hydrochloric acid and add a few drops of methyl red indicator.

Heat the solution to boiling-point and add $25\ cm^3$ of standard ammonium oxalate solution (about 0·5 M, standardised with permanganate) from a burette, slowly and with constant stirring. To the hot solution add dilute ammonia solution slowly and with stirring until the colour of the indicator changes from red to yellow, i.e. the solution is just alkaline. Filter and transfer the filtrate and washings quantitatively to a $250\ cm^3$ graduated flask, making up to the mark with water. Titrate $25\ cm^3$ aliquot parts of this solution, acidified with about $25\ cm^3$ of dilute sulphuric acid and heated to approximately 80 °C, with standard potassium permanganate solution (about 0·02 M).

Note. In this determination the calcium carbonate is first dissolved in hydrochloric acid

$$CaCO_3 + 2H^+ \rightarrow Ca^{2+} + CO_2(g) + H_2O$$

and the calcium is then precipitated as its oxalate by the addition of a known excess of ammonium oxalate solution:

$$Ca^{2+} + C_2O_4^{2-} \rightarrow CaC_2O_4(s)$$

The excess of oxalate is finally determined by titration with standard permanganate.

4. Weigh out accurately about 10 g of potassium hexacyanoferrate(II) (ferrocyanide) crystals, $K_4Fe(CN)_6.3H_2O$, and make up to $250\ cm^3$ of solution in a graduated flask. Titrate $25\ cm^3$ aliquot parts of this solution, acidified with about $25\ cm^3$ of dilute sulphuric acid, with standard potassium permanganate solution (about 0·02 M) until the colour changes from green-yellow to yellow-pink.

Calculate the molar ratio of $[Fe(CN)_6]^{4-}$ to MnO_4^- and hence derive an equation for the reaction which has occurred.

5. Weigh out accurately about 1 g of manganese dioxide and about 2·2 g of oxalic acid crystals, $H_2C_2O_4.2H_2O$. Transfer both solids quantitatively to a conical flask and add about $100\ cm^3$ of dilute sulphuric acid. Place a small funnel in the neck of the flask and boil gently until no undissolved particles of manganese dioxide remain:

$$MnO_2 + H_2C_2O_4 + 2H^+ \rightarrow Mn^{2+} + 2CO_2(g) + 2H_2O$$

Allow the solution to cool and dilute to exactly $250\ cm^3$ in a graduated flask. Determine the excess of oxalic acid in this solution by titrating $25\ cm^3$ aliquot parts with standard potassium permanganate solution (about 0·02 M) at approximately 80 °C in the presence of an excess of dilute sulphuric acid.

Hence calculate the percentage purity of the manganese dioxide.

6. Prepare $250\ cm^3$ of a solution containing about 0·8 g of hydroxylammonium chloride (accurately weighed) and about $150\ cm^3$ of a solution containing about 25 g of iron(III) alum. Boil $25\ cm^3$ aliquot parts of the hydroxylammonium chloride solution with approximately $25\ cm^3$ of the iron(III) alum solution (a substantial excess) and about

25 cm³ of dilute sulphuric acid for five minutes to ensure complete oxidation of the hydroxylammonium ions present. Dilute the resulting solution with about 50 cm³ of water and allow to cool to room temperature. Titrate the iron(II) produced with standard potassium permanganate solution (about 0·02 M) in the usual way.

From these results calculate the molar ratio of Fe^{3+} to hydroxylammonium ion, NH_3OH^+, deduce the nature of the nitrogen-containing product and hence deduce an equation for the reaction which has occurred under these conditions.

7. Weigh out accurately about 2 g of ammonium metavanadate, NH_4VO_3, and dissolve in dilute sulphuric acid (this solution may be regarded as containing the equivalent quantity of the oxide V_2O_5). Make up to exactly 250 cm³ in a graduated flask and use this solution for the following experiments.

(a) The oxide, V_2O_5, can be reduced by sulphur dioxide to a lower oxide which can be re-oxidised to its original state by potassium permanganate. To 25 cm³ of the solution add an approximately equal volume of dilute sulphuric acid and a few crystals of sodium sulphite. Boil gently until sulphur dioxide has been completely removed (test by smell or with dichromate paper). Cool and titrate the resulting solution with standard potassium permanganate solution (about 0·02 M). Deduce the change in oxidation number of the vanadium during the reduction and hence the formula of the lower oxide.

(b) The oxide, V_2O_5, can also be reduced by zinc amalgam to a different lower oxide which can be re-oxidised to its original state by potassium permanganate. Pipette 25 cm³ of the solution into a stoppered bottle containing zinc amalgam* and shake until the aqueous layer becomes bright blue, then green and finally pale lavender. Decant the aqueous layer as quickly as possible into a conical flask containing about 50 cm³ of iron(III) sulphate solution and immediately wash the amalgam by shaking with two portions of about 25 cm³ of dilute sulphuric acid. Add the washings to the solution in the flask and titrate this with standard potassium permanganate solution (about 0·02 M). The lower oxide of vanadium formed during the reduction is rapidly oxidised by air and this is prevented by transferring the reduced solution rapidly to an excess of iron(III) sulphate solution when the lower oxide reduces the iron(III) to iron(II). Deduce the change in oxidation number of the vanadium during the reduction and hence the formula of the lower oxide.

8. Formates are quantitatively oxidised by permanganate ion in sodium carbonate solution. Deduce an equation for the reaction which occurs by the following method.

Prepare 250 cm³ of a solution containing about 0·8 g of sodium formate (accurately weighed). Pipette 25 cm³ of this solution into a

*See Appendix II.

conical flask and add 10 cm³ of 10% sodium carbonate solution. Warm the solution and titrate with standard potassium permanganate solution (about 0·02 M) until the clear liquid is just pink. If difficulty is found in determining the exact end-point the following procedure should be adopted. Add the potassium permanganate solution from the burette until the solution is distinctly pink and note the burette reading. Acidify the solution strongly with dilute sulphuric acid and add 25 cm³ of 0·05 M sodium oxalate solution from a pipette (care!). Warm the mixture until the precipitate present initially has dissolved and the permanganate has been decolorised. Determine the excess of oxalate in this solution by titrating with standard potassium permanganate solution (about 0·02 M) at approximately 80 °C in the presence of an excess of dilute sulphuric acid. The volume of permanganate required to oxidise the formate may then be found.

Potassium dichromate, $K_2Cr_2O_7$

Preparation
Dissolve 2·5 g of chromium(III) chloride, $CrCl_3.6H_2O$, in about 20 cm³ of water, warming slightly if necessary to accelerate the process, and add the resulting solution slowly with shaking to 25 cm³ of 6 M potassium hydroxide solution. Add 50 cm³ of 10-volume hydrogen peroxide solution (this is a 3 × excess) and boil, when the solution will turn yellow:

$$Cr^{3+} + 3OH^- \rightarrow Cr(OH)_3(s)$$
(green)
$$2Cr(OH)_3(s) + 3O_2^{2-} \rightarrow 2CrO_4^{2-} + 2OH^- + 2H_2O,$$
(yellow)
i.e. $Cr(III) \rightarrow Cr(VI)$

Boil the yellow chromate solution to reduce the volume to about 30 cm³ and to decompose any excess of hydrogen peroxide. Allow to cool and gradually add an excess of dilute sulphuric acid when the solution will turn orange:

$$2CrO_4^{2-} + 2H^+ \rightleftharpoons Cr_2O_7^{2-} + H_2O$$

Evaporate the orange solution of potassium dichromate to about 25 cm³ and cool using an ice-bath. Filter off the orange crystals of potassium dichromate and recrystallise from nearly-boiling water. Filter off the crystals on a Hirsch funnel and dry them between filter papers.

Reactions
1. Dissolve some of the crystals in water and add dilute sulphuric acid to separate portions, followed by:
   (a) potassium iodide solution and a few drops of starch solution,
   (b) ammonium iron(II) sulphate solution (test the resulting solution with potassium thiocyanate solution),
   (c) a few drops of ethanol (use a concentrated solution of potassium

dichromate for this reaction)—note the smell of any gas evolved and any colour change.

2. Heat a few powdered crystals strongly, testing any gas evolved. Cool, add water, warm to dissolve the solid and note the colour.

3. Add a few drops of sodium hydroxide solution to a solution of the crystals and then add dilute sulphuric acid in an excess. Note any colour changes.

4. Warm a mixture of sodium chloride and powdered potassium dichromate with concentrated sulphuric acid. Note the colour of the vapour evolved.

TITRATIONS USING POTASSIUM DICHROMATE

1. Preparation of a standard solution of potassium dichromate

Potassium dichromate can be obtained as an 'Analar' reagent and its aqueous solution is much more stable than potassium permanganate. It is, therefore, used as a primary standard for redox titrations. It is a less powerful oxidising agent than potassium permanganate, but it can be used in the presence of chloride ions (see redox potentials).

In acid solution potassium dichromate is reduced to chromium(III) ion, this reaction involving a colour change from orange to green:

$$Cr_2O_7{}^{2-} + 14H^+ + 6e^- \rightarrow 2Cr^{3+} + 7H_2O, \qquad (12)$$
$$\text{i.e. } Cr(VI) \rightarrow Cr(III)$$

An indicator is essential when this half-reaction is used in titrimetric analysis as this colour change is gradual. In the titration of an iron(II) salt an aqueous solution of barium diphenylamine p-sulphonate gives a sharp colour change as soon as one drop of dichromate in an excess is added, provided phosphoric acid is present to form a complex with the iron(III) ions produced during the titration. The colour change is from blue-green to deep violet.

Weigh out accurately about 6 g of powdered 'Analar' potassium dichromate (previously dried in an oven at approximately 140 °C), dissolve it in water and dilute the solution to 1 litre in a graduated flask.

Calculate the molarity of the solution (it will be about 0·02 M). The molecular weight of potassium dichromate is 294·2.

2. Determination of the percentage of iron in iron(II) sulphate crystals

Weigh out accurately about 7 g of iron(II) sulphate crystals (preferably 'Analar') and make up to 250 cm³ of solution in a graduated flask with dilute sulphuric acid. Pipette 25 cm³ of this solution into a conical flask and add about 25 cm³ of dilute sulphuric acid, about 5 cm³ of syrupy phosphoric acid and 0·5 cm³ of barium diphenylamine p-sulphonate indicator.* Titrate with standard potassium dichromate solution (about

*See Appendix II.

0·02 M) until the solution turns a blue-green colour near the end-point. Continue adding the dichromate solution drop by drop until a permanent deep violet coloration is obtained.

The equations for the relevant half-reactions are:

$$Fe^{2+} - e^- \rightarrow Fe^{3+} \tag{3}$$

and,

$$Cr_2O_7^{2-} + 14H^+ + 6e^- \rightarrow 2Cr^{3+} + 7H_2O \tag{12}$$

Equation (3) $\times$ 6 + equation (12) gives:

$$Cr_2O_7^{2-} + 6Fe^{2+} + 14H^+ \rightarrow 2Cr^{3+} + 6Fe^{3+} + 7H_2O \tag{13}$$

It follows from equation (13) that

$$(MV)_{Fe^{2+}} = 6(MV)_{Cr_2O_7^{2-}}$$

Use this relation to calculate the molarity of the Fe^{2+} ions.

Then, concentration of Fe^{2+} ions $= (M_{Fe^{2+}} \times$ atomic weight of iron) g l^{-1}.

$\therefore$ Percentage of iron in the crystals

$$= \frac{\text{weight of iron in 1 litre of solution}}{4 \times \text{weight of crystals used}} \times 100$$

3. Determination of the percentage of iron in ammonium iron(III) alum

Tin(II) chloride may be used to reduce the iron(III) ions present in the alum to iron(II), as potassium dichromate can be used in the presence of chloride ions. The excess of tin(II) chloride is removed with mercury-(II) chloride solution:

$$2Fe^{3+} + Sn^{2+} \rightarrow 2Fe^{2+} + Sn^{4+} \tag{14}$$

$$2HgCl_2 + Sn^{2+} \rightarrow Hg_2Cl_2(s) + Sn^{4+} + 2Cl^- \tag{15}$$

Weigh out accurately about 12 g of the alum, dissolve in water and dilute the solution to exactly 250 cm³. Pipette 25 cm³ of this solution into a conical flask and add 5 cm³ of concentrated hydrochloric acid. Then add tin(II) chloride solution from a burette drop by drop until the yellow colour of iron(III) ions has *just* disappeared, followed by two or three more drops of the tin(II) chloride to ensure complete reduction to iron(II). A large excess of tin(II) chloride must *not* be used. Add 5 cm³ of saturated mercury(II) chloride solution, when a slight white precipitate of mercury(I) chloride should be produced (if no precipitate is obtained, insufficient tin(II) chloride has been added).

Titrate the reduced solution with standard potassium dichromate solution (about 0·02 M), adding about 5 cm³ of syrupy phosphoric acid and 0·5 cm³ of barium diphenylamine *p*-sulphonate indicator, until a permanent deep violet coloration is obtained.

Calculate the molarity of the Fe^{3+} ions using:

$$(MV)_{Fe^{3+}} = 6(MV)_{Cr_2O_7^{2-}} \text{ (see equations (13) and (14))}$$

Then, concentration of Fe^{3+} ions $= (M_{Fe^{3+}} \times$ atomic weight of iron) $g\,l^{-1}$.

$\therefore$ Percentage of iron in the alum

$$= \frac{\text{weight of iron in 1 litre of solution}}{4 \times \text{weight of alum used}} \times 100$$

Worked example

$25 \cdot 0$ cm³ of a solution containing iron(II) and iron(III) sulphates and dilute sulphuric acid required $21 \cdot 9$ cm³ of $0 \cdot 02$ M potassium dichromate solution for oxidation. A further $25 \cdot 0$ cm³ of the same solution, after reduction with tin(II) chloride solution, required $36 \cdot 6$ cm³ of the same dichromate solution for oxidation. Calculate the concentration of iron(II) and iron(III) in the solution in $g\,l^{-1}$.

The equations for the half reactions are

$$Fe^{2+} - e^- \rightarrow Fe^{3+}$$

and, $$Cr_2O_7^{2-} + 14H^+ + 6e^- \rightarrow 2Cr^{3+} + 7H_2O$$

giving the following equation for the overall reaction:

$$Cr_2O_7^{2-} + 6Fe^{2+} + 14H^+ \rightarrow 2Cr^{3+} + 6Fe^{3+} + 7H_2O \qquad (13)$$

Number of moles of $Cr_2O_7^{2-}$ required to oxidise Fe^{2+} only

$$= \frac{21 \cdot 9}{1000} \times 0 \cdot 02$$

$\therefore$ Number of moles of $Fe^{2+} = 6 \times \dfrac{21 \cdot 9}{1000} \times 0 \cdot 02$ (see equation (13))

$$= \frac{25 \cdot 0}{1000} \times M_{Fe^{2+}}$$

$\therefore M_{Fe^{2+}} = 6 \times \dfrac{21 \cdot 9}{1000} \times 0 \cdot 02 \times \dfrac{1000}{25 \cdot 0} = 0 \cdot 105$

and, concentration of $Fe^{2+} = 0 \cdot 105 \times 56$

$= 5 \cdot 88\ g\,l^{-1}$.

Number of moles of $Cr_2O_7^{2-}$ required to oxidise total iron after reduction

$$= \frac{36 \cdot 6}{1000} \times 0 \cdot 02$$

$\therefore$ Number of moles of Fe^{2+} and Fe^{3+}

$$= 6 \times \frac{36 \cdot 6}{1000} \times 0 \cdot 02 \quad \text{(see equation (13))}$$

$$= \frac{25 \cdot 0}{1000} \times M_{Fe}$$

$\therefore M_{Fe} = 6 \times \dfrac{36 \cdot 6}{1000} \times 0 \cdot 02 \times \dfrac{1000}{25 \cdot 0} = 0 \cdot 176$

and, concentration of total iron $= 0.176 \times 56$
$$= 9.84 \text{ g l}^{-1}.$$
$\therefore$ Concentration of $Fe^{3+} = 9.84 - 5.88$
$$= 3.96 \text{ g l}^{-1}.$$

Sodium thiosulphate, $Na_2S_2O_3.5H_2O$

Preparation

Dissolve 5 g of sodium sulphite crystals, $Na_2SO_3.7H_2O$, in 20 cm³ of water in a small evaporating dish. Heat the solution and add, with stirring, 1 g of powdered roll sulphur. Boil and filter any excess of sulphur while the mixture is still hot. Evaporate the filtrate to one-third volume and allow to cool. Add a little powdered sodium thiosulphate to the cold solution to assist crystallisation if necessary ('seeding'). Filter and dry the crystals between filter papers.

$$SO_3^{2-} \mid S \rightarrow S_2O_3^{2-}$$

The product may be recrystallised from nearly-boiling water, the cold solution being seeded as before.

Reactions

1. Warm a few crystals with dilute hydrochloric acid and identify any gas evolved.
2. Dissolve some of the crystals in water and to separate portions add:
   (a) iodine solution,
   (b) a little bromine water,
   (c) a little silver bromide and shake,
   (d) lead acetate solution and warm.
3. Heat a few crystals strongly, testing any gas evolved.

TITRATIONS USING SODIUM THIOSULPHATE

1. Preparation of a standard solution of sodium thiosulphate using potassium iodate

Crystals of hydrated sodium thiosulphate, $Na_2S_2O_3.5H_2O$, are obtainable in a state of high purity but it is not used as a primary standard as the water content is somewhat variable. An approximately 0.1 M solution can be made by dissolving 25 g of 'Analar' sodium thiosulphate in water and making up to 1 litre of solution. This solution can be standardised using an iodine solution of known molarity prepared by the oxidation of an excess of potassium iodide with potassium iodate in acid solution:

$$IO_3^- + 5I^- + 6H^+ \rightarrow 3I_2 + 3H_2O \qquad (16)$$

$$2S_2O_3^{2-} + I_2 \rightarrow 2I^- + S_4O_6^{2-} \qquad (17)$$

Weigh out accurately about 0.9 g of 'Analar' potassium iodate and make up to exactly 250 cm³ of solution. Pipette 25 cm³ of this solution into a conical flask, add 1·5 g of potassium iodide (or 15 cm³ of 10 per cent potassium iodide solution) and 15 cm³ of dilute sulphuric acid, and titrate the liberated iodine with the approximately 0·1 M sodium thiosulphate solution, adding 2 cm³ of starch solution when the solution is pale yellow. Continue the titration by adding the sodium thiosulphate solution from the burette one drop at a time until the deep blue colour disappears.

Calculate the molarity of the thiosulphate solution using:

$$(MV)_{thio} = 6(MV)_{IO_3^-}$$

a relation which follows from equations (16) and (17). The molecular weight of potassium iodate is 214·0.

Note. 1 mole of IO_3^- produces 3 moles of I_2 (see equation (16)) which, in turn, react with 6 moles of $S_2O_3^{2-}$ (see equation (17)).

2. Preparation of a standard solution of sodium thiosulphate using potassium dichromate

Weigh out accurately about 1·2 g of 'Analar' potassium dichromate and make up to exactly 250 cm³ of solution. Pipette 25 cm³ of this solution into a conical flask, add 1·5 g of potassium iodide and 15 cm³ of dilute sulphuric acid, and titrate the liberated iodine

$$Cr_2O_7^{2-} + 6I^- + 14H^+ \rightarrow 3I_2 + 2Cr^{3+} + 7H_2O \qquad (18)$$

with the approximately 0·1 M sodium thiosulphate solution, adding 2 cm³ of starch solution when a yellow-green colour is obtained. Continue the titration slowly, with thorough mixing of the solutions, until the blue colour just disappears and the solution is pale green (due to hydrated Cr^{3+} ions).

Calculate the molarity of the thiosulphate solution using:

$$(MV)_{thio} = 6(MV)_{Cr_2O_7^{2-}} \text{ (see equations (17) and (18)).}$$

3. Preparation of a standard solution of sodium thiosulphate using potassium permanganate

Pipette 25 cm³ of a standard solution of potassium permanganate (about 0·02 M) into a conical flask, add 1·5 g of potassium iodide and 15 cm³ of dilute sulphuric acid, and titrate the liberated iodine

$$2MnO_4^- + 10I^- + 16H^+ \rightarrow 5I_2 + 2Mn^{2+} + 8H_2O \qquad (19)$$

with the approximately 0·1 M sodium thiosulphate solution as in experiments 1 and 2, adding 2 cm³ of starch indicator near the end-point.

Calculate the molarity of the thiosulphate solution using:

$$(MV)_{thio} = 5(MV)_{MnO_4^-} \text{ (see equations (17) and (19)).}$$

4. Preparation of pure iodine and its use to prepare a standard solution of sodium thiosulphate

Heat approximately equal weights of potassium iodide and manganese dioxide with dilute sulphuric acid in a small evaporating dish. Collect the iodine which sublimes by means of an inverted funnel fitted to the evaporating dish as shown in Fig. 3.1:

$$MnO_2 + 2I^- + 4H^+ \rightarrow Mn^{2+} + I_2 + 2H_2O$$

Note. This preparation must be carried out in a fume cupboard.
Allow to cool, remove the sublimate and prepare 250 cm³ of a solution

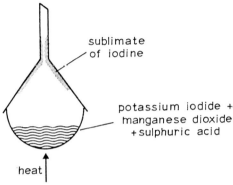

Fig. 3.1

containing about 3 g of the pure iodine and about 6 g of potassium iodide. Shake well to ensure that all the iodine has dissolved:

$$I_2 + I^- \rightleftharpoons I_3^-$$

This solution will be approximately 0·05 M.
Investigate the reactions of this solution as follows:
1. Dilute with water and add starch solution.
2. Shake with various organic solvents, e.g. benzene, chloroform, ethanol.
3. Add sodium thiosulphate solution gradually with shaking.
4. Add dilute sodium hydroxide solution.
5. Add dilute hydrochloric acid to a solution of sodium arsenite until the latter is slightly acidic and then dissolve a little sodium hydrogencarbonate in this solution. Shake well and add the iodine solution.

Titrate 25 cm³ aliquot parts of the standard iodine solution with the approximately 0·1 M sodium thiosulphate solution, adding 2 cm³ of starch indicator near the end-point.

Calculate the molarity of the thiosulphate solution using:

$$(MV)_{thio} = 2(MV)_{I_2} \text{ (see equation (17))}.$$

5. Determination of the percentage of copper in hydrated copper(II) sulphate

Weigh out accurately about 6 g of copper(II) sulphate crystals, dissolve in water and add sodium carbonate solution until a *faint* permanent blue precipitate of copper(II) carbonate is obtained. Dissolve this precipitate in the minimum volume of dilute acetic acid. This procedure removes free mineral acid in the solution. Dilute the clear solution to exactly 250 cm³. Pipette 25 cm³ of this solution into a conical flask, add 1·5 g of potassium iodide and titrate the liberated iodine

$$2Cu^{2+} + 4I^- \rightarrow 2CuI(s) + I_2 \qquad (20)$$

with standard sodium thiosulphate solution (about 0·1 M), adding 2 cm³ of starch indicator near the end-point.

Calculate the molarity of the copper(II) sulphate solution using:

$$(MV)_{Cu^{2+}} = (MV)_{thio} \text{ (see equations (17) and (20))}$$

Then, concentration of Cu^{2+} ions $= (M_{Cu^{2+}} \times \text{atomic weight of copper})$ g l^{-1}.

∴ Percentage of copper in the crystals

$$= \frac{\text{weight of copper in 1 litre of solution}}{4 \times \text{weight of crystals used}} \times 100$$

Note. Copper(I) iodide is precipitated during the reaction and, if difficulty is found in detecting the end-point, add about 10 cm³ of a 10 per cent aqueous solution of potassium thiocyanate when the blue colour of the starch–iodine complex begins to fade. The blue colour will become more intense and the titration should then be completed as rapidly as possible.

6. Determination of the percentage of available chlorine in sodium hypochlorite solution

When a solution of sodium hypochlorite is acidified chlorine is evolved:

$$NaOCl + 2HCl \rightarrow Cl_2 + NaCl + H_2O \qquad (21)$$

and the *available chlorine* refers to the chlorine liberated in this reaction.

One of the various makes of domestic bleach, e.g. 'Domestos', is a useful source of sodium hypochlorite. Dilute 10 cm³ of the bleach (measured by pipette) to exactly 250 cm³ in a graduated flask and titrate 25 cm³ aliquot parts of this solution, to which 1·5 g of potassium iodide and 10 cm³ of glacial acetic acid have been added, with standard sodium thiosulphate solution (about 0·1 M), adding 2 cm³ of starch indicator near the end-point.

Note. Acetic acid is used in this determination instead of sulphuric acid to reduce the error due to the presence of chlorate ion in the hypochlorite:

$$ClO_3^- + 6I^- + 6H^+ \rightarrow 3I_2 + Cl^- + 3H_2O$$

Sodium hypochlorite liberates iodine from potassium iodide in the presence of acetic acid:

$$OCl^- + 2I^- + 2H^+ \rightarrow I_2 + Cl^- + H_2O \qquad (22)$$

Calculate the molarity of the chlorine using:

$$2(MV)_{Cl_2} = (MV)_{thio} \quad \text{(see equations (17), (21) and (22))}$$

Then, concentration of chlorine = ($M_{Cl_2} \times$ molecular weight of chlorine) g l^{-1}.

∴ Percentage of available chlorine(w/v)

$$= \frac{\text{weight of chlorine in 1 litre of solution}}{10} \times 25$$

Note. 1 mole of Cl_2 is liberated from 1 mole of OCl^- (see equation (21)) which, in turn, liberates 1 mole of I_2 (see equation (22)), and 1 mole of I_2 reacts with 2 moles of $S_2O_3^{2-}$ (see equation (17)). The factor 25 is included in the expression for the percentage of available chlorine because the original bleach is diluted exactly 25 times.

7. Determination of the percentage purity of arsenic(III) oxide

The reaction between arsenic(III) oxide and iodine in aqueous solution is reversible:

$$As_2O_3 + 2I_2 + 2H_2O \rightleftharpoons As_2O_5 + 4HI \qquad (23)$$

but if the hydrogen iodide is removed from the solution by the addition of sodium hydrogencarbonate, the reaction proceeds quantitatively from left to right (a stronger alkali, such as sodium hydroxide, cannot be used as it would react with the iodine).

Weigh out accurately about 1·25 g of arsenic(III) oxide and dissolve it in 10 per cent sodium hydroxide solution. Transfer the solution quantitatively to a 250 cm^3 graduated flask, add a few drops of phenolphthalein and then dilute hydrochloric acid until the red colour of the indicator just disappears, i.e. the solution is just acidic. Add 2 g of sodium hydrogencarbonate, shake well to dissolve all the solid and dilute the solution to 250 cm^3.

Pipette 25 cm^3 of standard iodine solution (about 0·05 M) into a conical flask, add 2 g of sodium hydrogencarbonate and titrate with the arsenite solution in the burette, adding 2 cm^3 of starch indicator when the solution is pale yellow.

Note. Arsenite solutions should never be pipetted by mouth.

Calculate the molarity of the arsenite solution using:

$$2(MV)_{As_2O_3} = (MV)_{I_2} \quad \text{(see equation (23))}$$

Then, concentration of As_2O_3 = ($M_{As_2O_3} \times$ molecular weight of As_2O_3) g l^{-1}.

∴ Percentage purity of the As_2O_3

$$= \frac{\text{weight of } As_2O_3 \text{ in 1 litre of solution}}{4 \times \text{weight of } As_2O_3 \text{ used}} \times 100$$

8. Determination of the solubility of sulphur dioxide at room temperature

Prepare a saturated solution of sulphur dioxide in water at room temperature and dilute 10 cm³ (measured by burette) of this solution to 250 cm³ in a graduated flask. Place 50 cm³ (measured by means of a burette) of standard iodine solution (about 0·05 M) in a conical flask, add an approximately equal volume of water, 5 cm³ of dilute hydrochloric acid and then, *slowly and with constant stirring*, 25 cm³ of the diluted sulphur dioxide solution from a burette with the jet of the burette near the surface of the solution in the conical flask. Titrate the excess of iodine with standard sodium thiosulphate solution (about 0·1 M), adding 2 cm³ of starch indicator near the end-point.

Carry out at least two determinations in this way and calculate the solubility of sulphur dioxide at room temperature. The sulphur dioxide reacts with iodine according to the equation:

$$SO_2 + I_2 + 2H_2O \rightarrow H_2SO_4 + 2HI$$

∴ 1 mole of SO_2 reacts with 1 mole of I_2 and, from equation (17), 1 mole of I_2 reacts with 2 moles of $S_2O_3^{2-}$.

Worked example

3·00 g of Devarda's alloy were brought into solution and the solution was then diluted to 250 cm³. 25·0 cm³ of this diluted solution, after acidification and addition of an excess of potassium iodide, reacted with 22·5 cm³ of 0·100 M sodium thiosulphate solution. Calculate the percentage of copper in the alloy.

The equations for the reactions are

$$Cu - 2e^- \rightarrow Cu^{2+} \tag{24}$$

$$2Cu^{2+} + 4I^- \rightarrow 2CuI(s) + I_2 \tag{20}$$

$$2S_2O_3^{2-} + I_2 \rightarrow 2I^- + S_4O_6^{2-} \tag{17}$$

Number of moles of $S_2O_3^{2-}$ reacting $= \dfrac{22 \cdot 5}{1000} \times 0 \cdot 100$

∴ Number of moles of $Cu^{2+} = \dfrac{22 \cdot 5}{1000} \times 0 \cdot 100$ (from equations (17) and (20))

$$= \dfrac{25 \cdot 0}{1000} \times M_{Cu^{2+}}$$

∴ $M_{Cu} = \dfrac{22 \cdot 5}{1000} \times 0 \cdot 100 \times \dfrac{1000}{25 \cdot 0}$ (from equation (24))

$$= 0 \cdot 090$$

∴ Concentration of copper $= 0 \cdot 090 \times 63 \cdot 5$ g l⁻¹

and, percentage of copper in the alloy $= \dfrac{0 \cdot 090 \times 63 \cdot 5}{4 \times 3 \cdot 00} \times 100$

$$= 47 \cdot 6.$$

Additional Problems

1. Weigh out accurately about 0·9 g of potassium iodate and make it up to exactly 250 cm³ of solution. Pipette 25 cm³ of this solution into a conical flask, add 1·5 g of potassium iodide and 15 cm³ of dilute sulphuric acid and titrate the liberated iodine with standard sodium thiosulphate solution (about 0·1 M), adding 2 cm³ of starch indicator near the end-point, i.e. when the solution is pale yellow.

Deduce an equation for the reaction between iodate and iodide ions in acid solution.

2. When a solution containing iodide and iodate ions is acidified iodine is liberated:

$$IO_3^- + 5I^- + 6H^+ \rightarrow 3I_2 + 3H_2O$$

The free iodine may be titrated with standard sodium thiosulphate solution so that a standard solution containing a known weight of 'Analar' potassium iodate and a slight excess of potassium iodide can be used in the determination of acids.

Prepare 250 cm³ of a solution containing about 1 g of 'Analar' potassium iodate and add 50 cm³ of this solution to exactly 25 cm³ of approximately 0·05 M sulphuric acid in which about 1·5 g of potassium iodide has been dissolved. Titrate the liberated iodine with standard sodium thiosulphate solution (about 0·1 M), adding 2 cm³ of starch indicator near the end-point.

Note. The amounts of potassium iodate and potassium iodide used in the titration both represent a slight excess, so that the amount of acid used is insufficient to liberate *all* the iodine.

Calculate the molarity of the sulphuric acid using:

$$2(MV)_{H_2SO_4} = (MV)_{thio}$$

(derive this relation from the relevant equations)

3. Investigate the reaction between bromine and sodium thiosulphate as follows.

(*a*) Prepare 100 cm³ of approximately 0·05 M bromine solution by accurate dilution of saturated bromine water (the dilution factor will be about 4). To 25 cm³ aliquot parts of the diluted solution (measured by burette) add 1·5 g of potassium iodide and titrate the liberated iodine:

$$Br_2 + 2I^- \rightarrow 2Br^- + I_2$$

with standard sodium thiosulphate solution (about 0·1 M), using starch as indicator. Calculate the molarity of the diluted bromine water and hence of the saturated bromine water.

(*b*) Titrate 25 cm³ aliquot parts of the saturated bromine water directly with the same thiosulphate solution until the red colour of the bromine is just destroyed.

(*c*) Carry out suitable qualitative tests on the product in (*b*), including the use of indicators, to determine the anions present.

From these results calculate the molar ratio of Br_2 to $S_2O_3^{2-}$ and hence derive an equation for the reaction between bromine and thiosulphate ions.

4. Investigate the reaction between iodate and iodide ions in the presence of a high concentration of hydrochloric acid as follows.

Prepare 100 cm³ of a solution containing about 0·6 g of potassium iodide (accurately weighed) and pipette 25 cm³ of this solution into a stoppered bottle. Add 50 cm³ of concentrated hydrochloric acid and 5 cm³ of chloroform and titrate with standard potassium iodate solution (about 0·02 M, prepared by direct weighing—molecular weight of $KIO_3 = 214·0$). When the solution becomes pale brown shake the stoppered bottle vigorously so that the chloroform layer turns violet due to the iodine present. Continue to add the potassium iodate solution from the burette a little at a time, shaking well after each addition, until the chloroform layer loses the last trace of violet colour and becomes pale yellow.

Calculate the molar ratio of I^- to IO_3^- and hence deduce an equation for the reaction between iodate and iodide ions under these conditions.

5. Investigate the reaction between hydrazine and potassium iodate in the presence of concentrated hydrochloric acid as follows.

Prepare an approximately 0·025 M solution of hydrazine sulphate, $N_2H_4.H_2SO_4$ (about 3–4 g l⁻¹—the exact weight used must be known) and pipette 25 cm³ of the solution into a stoppered bottle. Add 30 cm³ of concentrated hydrochloric acid, 20 cm³ of water and 5 cm³ of chloroform and titrate with standard potassium iodate solution (about 0·02 M, prepared by direct weighing—molecular weight of potassium iodate = 214·0). The potassium iodate solution should be added slowly from the burette, shaking vigorously after each addition, until there is no trace of violet colour in the chloroform layer.

Calculate the molar ratio of N_2H_4 to IO_3^- and hence deduce the nature of the oxidation product of the hydrazine. Write an equation for the reaction which occurs under these conditions.

Note. In the presence of concentrated hydrochloric acid the iodate is reduced to iodine monochloride:

$$IO_3^- + Cl^- + 6H^+ + 4e^- \rightleftharpoons ICl + 3H_2O$$

which is hardly extracted by the chloroform. The iodine which is liberated initially gives a violet colour in the chloroform layer but this disappears when oxidation of the iodine to iodine monochloride is complete.

6. Investigate the reaction between copper(II) sulphate solution and ammonia solution by the following method.

When dilute ammonia solution is added to copper(II) sulphate solution a blue precipitate of copper(II) hydroxide is formed provided the ammonia is not in an excess. Determine how the amount of copper(II) sulphate used to form the precipitate varies with the amount of ammonia used. For this purpose use 0·1 M copper(II) sulphate solution (determine its exact concentration by titration with standard sodium thiosulphate solution—see page 40) and 0·1 M ammonia solution. Use a constant volume (25 cm³) of the copper(II) sulphate solution and add various amounts of the ammonia solution (0–100 cm³). In each case mix the reactants thoroughly, filter off the precipitate formed and titrate the filtrate and washings with standard sodium thiosulphate solution (about 0·1 M).

Calculate the amount of unused copper(II) ions in each case and hence the amount used to form the precipitate. Plot the volume of copper(II) sulphate used to form the precipitate (y axis) against the volume of ammonia added (x axis) and draw what conclusions you can from the results.

For further reading

1. L. C. Roselaar, *Systematic Physical Chemistry*, pp. 179–188. John Murray, 1975.
   The electronic theory of oxidation and reduction, including redox potentials.
2. E. E. Aynsley and A. B. Littlewood, *Principles of Titrimetric Analysis*, pp. 31–33 and 37–40. The Royal Institute of Chemistry, 1962.
3. A. G. Sharpe, *Principles of Oxidation and Reduction* (Second Edition). The Royal Institute of Chemistry, 1968.
   This monograph includes a comprehensive list of standard redox potentials.
4. A. I. Vogel, *A Textbook of Quantitative Inorganic Analysis* (Third Edition), pp. 83–103. Longmans, 1962.
   The theory of redox titrations.
5. D. B. Sowerby and M. F. A. Dove, 'Oxidation States in Inorganic Compounds', *Education in Chemistry,* 1964, 2, **1**, 83–90.

4 Precipitation Titrations

In a precipitation titration, ions combine to form a relatively insoluble precipitate, e.g. in the titration of silver nitrate solution with a solution of a chloride, silver chloride is precipitated (solubility product = $1·8 \times 10^{-10}$ mol² l⁻² at 25 °C):

$$Ag^+(aq) + Cl^-(aq) \rightarrow AgCl(s)$$

D

and with potassium thiocyanate solution, silver thiocyanate is precipitated (solubility product $= 1 \cdot 0 \times 10^{-12}$ $mol^2\, l^{-2}$ at 25 °C):

$$Ag^+(aq) + SCN^-(aq) \rightarrow AgSCN(s)$$

The stoichiometric point in a precipitation titration may be determined as follows.

(a) By *Mohr's method*, in which potassium chromate solution is used as an indicator in the determination of chlorides and bromides *in neutral solution* by silver nitrate. At first, addition of silver nitrate solution causes the precipitation of the silver halide:

$$Ag^+(aq) + Hal^-(aq) \rightarrow AgHal(s)$$

When all the halide ions have been precipitated in this way, addition of further silver ion produces a red precipitate of silver chromate (solubility product $= 1 \cdot 3 \times 10^{-12}$ $mol^3\, l^{-3}$ at 25 °C):

$$2Ag^+(aq) + CrO_4{}^{2-}(aq) \rightarrow Ag_2CrO_4(s)$$

The end-point of the titration is, therefore, shown by the appearance of a reddish tinge. Silver chromate is soluble even in weak acids, so that acid solutions must be neutralised before titration, and in alkaline solution silver oxide would be precipitated:

$$2Ag^+(aq) + 2OH^-(aq) \rightarrow Ag_2O(s) + H_2O$$

Although the solubility product of silver chromate is lower than that of silver chloride, the expression for the solubility product of the chromate ($K_{sp} = [Ag^+]^2[CrO_4{}^{2-}]$) includes the *square* of the silver ion concentration (*cf.* silver chloride for which the solubility product expression is $K_{sp} = [Ag^+][Cl^-]$), so that it is, in fact, more soluble than silver chloride under these conditions. Also, the chloride ion concentration is high at the beginning of the titration, so that silver chloride is precipitated first.

(b) By means of an *adsorption indicator*. The principle involved in this method is the change in adsorption properties of the indicator near the stoichiometric point. The indicator is an organic dye, such as fluorescein, which is only adsorbed on the surface of the silver halide precipitate when all the halide ions have been precipitated. With fluorescein, the white precipitate of silver chloride in a yellow-green solution changes to a pink precipitate.

(c) By *Volhard's method*, in which the concentration of silver ions in a solution is determined by titration with standard potassium thiocyanate solution, using a solution of ammonium iron(III) alum in dilute nitric acid as indicator. At first, the thiocyanate ions added react with the silver ions to give a white precipitate of silver thiocyanate:

$$Ag^+(aq) + SCN^-(aq) \rightarrow AgSCN(s)$$

When this reaction is complete, the addition of a further amount of thiocyanate ion produces the deep red colour of the thiocyanatoiron(III) complex ion:

$$Fe^{3+}(aq) + SCN^-(aq) \rightarrow [FeSCN]^{2+}$$

The end-point is thus shown by the appearance of the first faint red tinge.

Chlorides, bromides and iodides may be determined in acid solution by this method. The silver halide is precipitated by adding an excess of standard silver nitrate solution and the excess is determined by back-titration with standard potassium thiocyanate solution.

Silver nitrate, $AgNO_3$

Preparation

Add 4 cm³ of 40 per cent 'Analar' nitric acid ('Analar' concentrated nitric acid contains about 70 per cent nitric acid) to 2 g of silver in an evaporating dish. Evaporate the resulting solution carefully to dryness on a steam bath and recrystallise the product from hot water.

$$3Ag + 4HNO_3 \rightarrow 3AgNO_3 + NO(g) + 2H_2O$$

Reactions

1. Heat a few crystals, testing any gas evolved.
2. To a solution in *distilled* water add:
   (*a*) sodium hydroxide solution,
   (*b*) dilute ammonia solution gradually until in an excess,
   (*c*) solutions of sodium chloride, bromide and iodide (separately); add (*i*) dilute nitric acid and (*ii*) dilute ammonia solution to the precipitate formed in each case,
   (*d*) potassium chromate solution and again add (*i*) dilute nitric acid and (*ii*) dilute ammonia solution to the precipitate,
   (*e*) potassium thiocyanate solution, followed by (*i*) dilute nitric acid and (*ii*) dilute ammonia solution as in (*c*) and (*d*).

TITRATIONS USING SILVER NITRATE*

1. Preparation of a standard solution of silver nitrate (Mohr's method)

Weigh out accurately about 4 g of 'Analar' silver nitrate, dissolve it in distilled water and dilute to 250 cm³ in a graduated flask. Mix thoroughly before use. The exact molarity of this solution can be calculated, as 'Analar' silver nitrate is at least 99·9 per cent pure (molecular weight of $AgNO_3$ = 169·9).

Alternatively, an approximately 0·1 M solution can be prepared using recrystallised silver nitrate and standardised with 'Analar' sodium chloride which is used as a primary standard. Weigh out accurately about 1·5 g of 'Analar' sodium chloride, dissolve it in distilled water and dilute to 250 cm³ in a graduated flask. Calculate the molarity of this solution (a 1 M solution contains 58·44 g of NaCl per litre). Titrate

*Note. Distilled water should always be used in silver nitrate titrations.

25 cm³ aliquot parts of this solution with the approximately 0·1 M silver nitrate solution:

$$Ag^+(aq) + Cl^-(aq) \rightarrow AgCl(s) \qquad (1)$$

using (*i*) 1 cm³ of 5 per cent potassium chromate solution,
      (*ii*) 10 drops of either fluorescein or dichlorofluorescein,

as indicator. In (*i*) the appearance of a faint permanent reddish tinge indicates the end-point and in (*ii*) the precipitate of silver chloride turns pink at the end-point. Compare the results obtained by the two methods.

Calculate the molarity of the silver nitrate solution using:

$$(MV)_{Ag^+} = (MV)_{Cl^-}$$

a relation which follows from equation (1), as 1 mole of Ag^+ ions reacts with 1 mole of Cl^- ions.

2. Preparation of constant boiling-point hydrochloric acid and determination of its composition*

When an aqueous solution of hydrochloric acid is boiled either hydrogen chloride or water vapour is lost, according to whether the solution is more or less concentrated than the constant boiling-point mixture, until the composition is practically constant at a given pressure. A constant boiling-point (or *azeotropic*) mixture is one which boils at a constant temperature and distils without change in composition, the composition of the mixture depending on the pressure at which it is distilled.

Dilute about 25 cm³ of concentrated hydrochloric acid (about 10 M) with water to give approximately 50 cm³ of acid of density 1·10 g cm⁻³. Check the density of the acid by means of a hydrometer. Distil the diluted acid in a 100 cm³ distillation flask fitted with a thermometer and a condenser in the usual way. When about half the acid has distilled collect a further 10 cm³ in a small 'Pyrex' flask, noting the temperature at which the mixture distils and the atmospheric pressure at the time of distillation. Determine the composition of this constant boiling-point mixture by the following method.

Dilute 10 cm³ of constant boiling-point hydrochloric acid (measured by burette) accurately to 500 cm³ in a graduated flask (the acid is approximately 6 M). Pipette 25 cm³ of the diluted acid into a conical flask and add about 1 g of 'Analar' calcium carbonate (chloride-free) to neutralise the acid. This is an appreciable excess of calcium carbonate and the concentration of chloride ions will be unchanged in this process. The neutral solution can be titrated with standard silver nitrate solution (about 0·1 M), using potassium chromate as indicator (1 cm³ of a 5 per cent solution).

Calculate the molarity of the diluted acid using:

$$(MV)_{HCl} = (MV)_{Ag^+}$$

*See experiment (7) for an alternative method.

a relation which follows from the equations

$$CaCO_3 + 2H^+Cl^- \rightarrow Ca^{2+}(Cl^-)_2 + CO_2(g) + H_2O$$
and, $$Ag^+(aq) + Cl^-(aq) \rightarrow AgCl(s)$$

and hence the molarity of the constant boiling-point acid.

3. Determination of the number of molecules of water of crystallisation in barium chloride crystals

Weigh out accurately about 3 g of barium chloride crystals and make up to 250 cm^3 of solution in a graduated flask. Pipette 25 cm^3 of this solution into a conical flask and add about 1 g of sodium sulphate crystals to precipitate the barium ions, which would otherwise react with the potassium chromate indicator to precipitate barium chromate:

$$Ba^{2+}(Cl^-)_2 + SO_4^{2-} \rightarrow BaSO_4(s) + 2Cl^- \qquad (2)$$

The concentration of chloride ions in the solution will be unchanged in this process. Titrate the solution with standard silver nitrate solution (about 0.1 M), using potassium chromate as indicator (1 cm^3 of a 5 per cent solution).

Calculate the molarity of the barium chloride solution using:

$$2(MV)_{BaCl_2} = (MV)_{Ag^+}$$

a relation which follows from equations (1) and (2), as 1 mole of $BaCl_2$ gives 2 moles of Cl^- which react with 2 moles of Ag^+ ions.

Then, molecular weight of hydrated barium chloride

$$= \frac{4 \times \text{weight of crystals used}}{M_{BaCl_2}}$$

$$= \text{molecular weight of anhydrous salt } (208.2) + 18n$$

from which n, the number of molecules of water of crystallisation, can be calculated.

Note. The removal of barium ions is not necessary if an adsorption indicator such as fluorescein is used.

4. Determination of the composition of a mixture of sodium chloride and hydrochloric acid*

(*a*) Titrate 25 cm^3 aliquot parts of the solution with standard sodium hydroxide solution (about 0.1 M), using phenolphthalein as indicator. Calculate the molarity of the hydrochloric acid using:

$$(MV)_{HCl} = (MV)_{NaOH}$$

a relation which follows from the equation

$$H^+ + OH^- \rightarrow H_2O$$

Then, concentration of HCl $= (M_{HCl} \times \text{molecular weight of HCl}) \text{ g l}^{-1}$.

*The solution should be about 0.08 M with respect to each component of the mixture.

(*b*) Pipette a separate 25 cm³ of the solution into a conical flask and add about 1 g of 'Analar' calcium carbonate to neutralise the acid. Determine the total chloride ion concentration by titration with standard silver nitrate solution (about 0·1 M), using either potassium chromate or fluorescein as indicator. Calculate the molarity of the chloride ion using:

$$(MV)_{Cl^-} = (MV)_{Ag^+} \text{ (see equation (1))}$$

Then, total concentration of Cl^- ion $= (M_{Cl^-} \times$ atomic weight of chlorine) g l⁻¹

$$= x$$

But, concentration of Cl^- ion as $HCl = (M_{HCl} \times$ atomic weight of chlorine) g l⁻¹

$$= y$$

∴ Concentration of Cl^- ion as sodium chloride

$$= x - y$$

and, concentration of NaCl $= (x - y) \dfrac{58\cdot44}{35\cdot45}$ g l⁻¹.

5. Determination of the composition of a mixture of sodium chloride and sodium bromide

The two halides should be present in the mixture in approximately equal amounts. Weigh out accurately about 2 g of the mixture and make up to 250 cm³ of solution in a graduated flask. Titrate 25 cm³ aliquot parts of this solution with standard silver nitrate solution (about 0·1 M), using potassium chromate or fluorescein as indicator, to determine the total halide.

Let x = weight of mixture used, consisting of a g of sodium chloride and b g of sodium bromide. Then:

$$a + b = x \qquad \text{(I)}$$

But, number of moles of Cl^- reacting $= \dfrac{a}{58\cdot44} \times \dfrac{25\cdot0}{250}$

and, number of moles of Br^- reacting $= \dfrac{b}{102\cdot9} \times \dfrac{25\cdot0}{250}$

∴ Number of moles of Ag^+ reacting $= \dfrac{(MV)_{Ag^+}}{1000}$

= total number of moles of Cl^- and Br^- reacting

$$= \left(\dfrac{a}{58\cdot44} + \dfrac{b}{102\cdot9} \right) / 10 \qquad \text{(II)}$$

The values of a and b can then be found by solving the simultaneous equations (I) and (II).

6. Preparation of a standard solution of potassium thiocyanate (Volhard's method)

Weigh out about 2·5 g of potassium thiocyanate and make it up to 250 cm³ in a graduated flask. This solution will be about 0·1 M. Titrate 25 cm³ aliquot parts of standard silver nitrate solution (about 0·1 M) with this potassium thiocyanate solution, using 1 cm³ of saturated ammonium iron(III) alum solution, in the presence of about 15 cm³ of dilute nitric acid, as indicator. A white precipitate of silver thiocyanate is produced initially:

$$Ag^+(aq) + SCN^-(aq) \rightarrow AgSCN(s) \tag{3}$$

and, as further thiocyanate is added, a reddish tinge is produced which disappears on shaking. Finally, at the end-point, a faint red tinge is produced which does not disappear on shaking.

Calculate the molarity of the potassium thiocyanate solution using:

$$(MV)_{SCN^-} = (MV)_{Ag^+} \text{ (see equation (3))}.$$

7. Determination of the concentration of hydrochloric acid (Volhard's method)

Dilute 10 cm³ of constant boiling-point hydrochloric acid* (measured by burette) accurately to 500 cm³ in a graduated flask (the acid is approximately 6 M). Alternatively concentrated hydrochloric acid (approximately 10 M) may be used; 10 cm³ (measured by burette) should be accurately diluted to 1 litre in a graduated flask.

Pipette 25 cm³ of the diluted acid into a conical flask, add about 15 cm³ of dilute nitric acid and then 50 cm³ of standard silver nitrate solution (about 0·1 M). The latter, which should be measured accurately by pipette, represents an excess. Shake the mixture thoroughly and filter off the precipitate of silver chloride, which is more soluble than silver thiocyanate and would react with the thiocyanate added subsequently. Wash the precipitate thoroughly and titrate the filtrate and washings with standard potassium thiocyanate solution (about 0·1 M), using 1 cm³ of saturated ammonium iron(III) alum solution as indicator, to determine the excess of silver nitrate.

Note. No preliminary neutralisation of the acid is necessary if Volhard's method is used (*cf.* experiment (2) in which potassium chromate is used as indicator).

$$Ag^+(aq) + Cl^-(aq) \rightarrow AgCl(s) \tag{1}$$

$$Ag^+(aq) + SCN^-(aq) \rightarrow AgSCN(s) \tag{3}$$

Calculate the volume of the excess of silver nitrate using:

$$(MV)_{Ag^+} = (MV)_{SCN^-} \text{ (see equation (3))}$$

and hence the volume which reacts with the hydrochloric acid. Calculate the molarity of the diluted acid using:

*See experiment (2).

$$(MV)_{\text{HCl}} = (MV)_{\text{Ag}^+} \text{ (see equation (1))}$$

Hence calculate the molarity of the original hydrochloric acid.

8. Determination of bromide (Volhard's method)

Weigh out accurately about 3 g of potassium bromide and make it up to exactly 250 cm³ of solution. Pipette 25 cm³ of this solution into a conical flask, acidify with about 15 cm³ of dilute nitric acid and add 50 cm³ of standard silver nitrate solution (about 0·1 M). The latter, which should be measured accurately by pipette, represents an excess. Shake the mixture thoroughly and determine the excess of silver nitrate by titration with standard potassium thiocyanate solution (about 0·1 M), using 1 cm³ of saturated ammonium iron(III) alum solution as indicator.

Note. It is not necessary to filter off the precipitate of silver bromide (*cf.* experiment (7)), as silver bromide is less soluble than silver thiocyanate.

Calculate the volume of the excess of silver nitrate using:

$$(MV)_{\text{Ag}^+} = (MV)_{\text{SCN}^-} \text{ (see equation (3))}$$

and hence the volume which reacts with the potassium bromide solution. Calculate the molarity of the potassium bromide solution using:

$$(MV)_{\text{Br}^-} = (MV)_{\text{Ag}}$$

a relation which follows from the equation for the precipitation of silver bromide:

$$\text{Ag}^+(\text{aq}) + \text{Br}^-(\text{aq}) \rightarrow \text{AgBr(s)}$$

Worked example

9·50 g of a mixture of potassium chloride and potassium bromide were made up to 1 litre of solution. 25·0 cm³ of this solution required 25·5 cm³ of 0·100 M silver nitrate solution for complete precipitation. Calculate the percentage composition of the mixture.

Let the weight of potassium chloride in the mixture be x g.

Then, molarity of potassium chloride

$$= \frac{x}{39\cdot1 + 35\cdot5} = \frac{x}{74\cdot6}$$

Weight of potassium bromide in the mixture $= (9\cdot50 - x)$ g and, molarity of potassium bromide

$$= \frac{(9\cdot50 - x)}{39\cdot1 + 79\cdot9} = \frac{(9\cdot50 - x)}{119\cdot0}$$

The equation for the reaction is

$$\text{Ag}^+(\text{aq}) + \text{Hal}^-(\text{aq}) \rightarrow \text{AgHal(s)} \quad \text{where Hal} = \text{Cl or Br}$$

∴ Number of moles of Cl⁻ + Br⁻ = number of moles of Ag⁺

i.e. $\left[\dfrac{x}{74\cdot 6} + \dfrac{(9\cdot 50 - x)}{119\cdot 0} \right] \dfrac{25\cdot 0}{1000} = \dfrac{25\cdot 5}{1000} \times 0\cdot 100$

and, $x = 4\cdot 43$

∴ Percentage composition of the mixture is

potassium chloride, $\dfrac{4\cdot 43}{9\cdot 50} \times 100 = 46\cdot 6$

potassium bromide, $\dfrac{9\cdot 50 - 4\cdot 43}{9\cdot 50} \times 100 = 53\cdot 4$.

Additional Problems

1. X is a complex of mercury of formula $Hg(NH_3)_aCl_b$. Determine the values of a and b by the following method.

(a) Weigh out accurately about 0·6 g of X and dissolve it by warming with exactly 50 cm³ of 0·1 M hydrochloric acid. Pass hydrogen sulphide into the resulting solution while it is still warm to precipitate the mercury as its sulphide, HgS. Continue passing the hydrogen sulphide until the precipitate is completely black and the liquid above it is quite clear. Boil off the excess of hydrogen sulphide and then filter off the mercury(II) sulphide precipitate. Wash the precipitate thoroughly with water and dilute the filtrate and washings (after cooling) to 100 cm³ in a graduated flask.

(b) Titrate 25 cm³ aliquot parts of the solution from (a) with standard sodium hydroxide solution (about 0·1 M), using methyl orange as indicator.

(c) Dilute the neutral solution from (b) with about 50 cm³ of water and determine the total chloride by titration with standard silver nitrate solution (about 0·1 M), using potassium chromate as indicator.

2. Y is a double salt of potassium and copper(II) chloride. Dissolve about 2·5 g of Y (accurately weighed) in water and dilute to exactly 250 cm³. Find the simplest formula of Y as follows.

(a) Pipette 50 cm³ of the solution into a conical flask, add about 1·5 g of potassium iodide and titrate the liberated iodine with standard sodium thiosulphate solution (about 0·1 M), using starch as indicator.

(b) Pipette 25 cm³ of the solution into a conical flask, add about 15 cm³ of dilute nitric acid and then exactly 50 cm³ of 0·1 M silver nitrate solution. Shake the mixture thoroughly and filter off the precipitate of silver chloride. Wash the precipitate well with water and titrate the filtrate and washings with standard potassium thiocyanate solution (about 0·1 M), using 1 cm³ of saturated ammonium iron(III) alum solution as indicator.

Calculate the molar ratio of Cl⁻ to Cu²⁺ and hence deduce the empirical formula of Y.

For further reading

1. L. C. Roselaar, *Systematic Physical Chemistry*, pp. 166–169. John Murray, 1975.
   The solubility product principle and its applications.
2. A. I. Vogel, *A Textbook of Quantitative Inorganic Analysis* (Third Edition), pp. 72–83. Longmans, 1962.
   The theory of precipitation titrations.

5 Complexometric Titrations

The formation of complex ions is widely used in chemical analysis. The ease of formation of a complex ion at a given temperature is measured by its *stability constant* (K_{stab}), e.g.

$$Zn^{2+} + 4NH_3 \rightleftharpoons [Zn(NH_3)_4]^{2+}$$

$$K_{stab} = \frac{[\{Zn(NH_3)_4\}^{2+}]}{[Zn^{2+}][NH_3]^4} = 1 \cdot 1 \times 10^9 \text{ mol}^{-4} \text{ l}^4 \text{ at } 25\,°C$$

It will be clear that the higher the stability constant the greater the stability of the complex ion.

If complex formation is to be used in titrimetric analysis a high stability constant is necessary. The formation of the complex tetra-amminezinc(II) ion, $[Zn(NH_3)_4]^{2+}$, involves a number of intermediate steps and four complex ions $[Zn(NH_3)_n]^{2+}$ (where $n = 1, 2, 3$ or 4) would be present in substantial amounts during a possible titration. As the value of K_{stab} for each of these steps is approximately equal a sharp end-point would not be obtained. This is in marked contrast to the reaction between a strong acid and a strong base:

$$H^+ + OH^- \rightleftharpoons H_2O$$

for which the equilibrium constant, $K = \dfrac{[H_2O]}{[H^+][OH^-]} = 5 \cdot 5 \times 10^{15}$ mol^{-1} l at 25 °C.

For titrimetric purposes it is desirable that the complex should be formed in one step. Ethylenediamine tetra-acetic acid(EDTA)

$$\begin{matrix} HOOC–CH_2 \\ \\ HOOC–CH_2 \end{matrix} \Big\rangle N–CH_2–CH_2–N \Big\langle \begin{matrix} CH_2–COOH \\ \\ CH_2–COOH \end{matrix}$$

is an excellent complexing agent which forms a very stable complex with zinc ($K_{stab} = 1 \cdot 3 \times 10^{16}$ mol^{-1} l at 20 °C) and with most other metal ions.

It can be represented as H_4Y where the Y^{4-} cation is the strong complexing agent containing two nitrogen and four oxygen (from the carbonyl of the acetate groups) atoms which are capable of forming co-ordinate bonds using their lone-pair electrons. When one molecule of EDTA reacts with a metal ion such as Zn^{2+} all six co-ordinating atoms become attached to the same metal ion with the formation of a ring structure known as a *chelate* (Fig. 5.1).

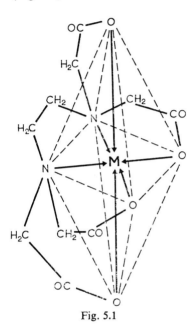

Fig. 5.1

The disodium salt of EDTA, $Na_2H_2Y.2H_2O$, is normally used in EDTA titrations as it is available in 'Analar' form which can be used as a primary standard. The reaction of a metal such as zinc with the disodium salt may be represented by the equation:

$$Zn^{2+} + H_2Y^{2-} \rightleftharpoons ZnY^{2-} + 2H^+$$

and EDTA is widely used to determine metals in what is known as a *complexometric titration*. It will be seen from this equation that the pH of the solution plays an important part in EDTA titrations as the metal-EDTA complex will be less stable at low pH. It is, therefore, necessary to maintain the solution at a suitable pH value during a titration, e.g. Zn^{2+} and Mg^{2+} can be titrated with EDTA using an ammonia–ammonium chloride buffer solution of pH 10.

The end-point of an EDTA titration is detected by means of a metal indicator such as Eriochrome Black T, which forms a coloured complex with the metal ion being titrated. The free indicator must have a different colour from the metal–indicator complex, which must be less stable than the metal–EDTA complex. At the beginning of the titration the metal-indicator complex is present but as the EDTA is added the free metal ions are gradually complexed to form the metal–EDTA compound until, at the stoichiometric point, the metal is removed from the metal-indicator complex and the colour of the free indicator is seen:

$$\text{Metal–Indicator} + \text{EDTA} \rightarrow \text{Metal–EDTA} + \text{Indicator}$$
$$(red) \hspace{5.5cm} (blue)$$

1. Preparation of a standard solution of EDTA

'Analar' disodium dihydrogen ethylenediamine tetra-acetate can be used as a primary standard if it is first dried at 80 °C. A 0·1 M solution is prepared by weighing out accurately 37·22 g of the disodium salt, dissolving in distilled (or, better, de-ionised) water and diluting to 1 litre in a graduated flask.

Carry out the following qualitative tests using this solution.

(a) Add an equal volume of ammonia–ammonium chloride buffer solution (pH 10)* to a few drops of 0·1 M copper(II) sulphate solution diluted to 5 cm³ with water. Add the EDTA solution drop by drop to this solution with thorough mixing and note any change in colour which occurs. Can you suggest an explanation for this observation? (K_{stab} for the $[Cu(NH_3)_4]^{2+}$ complex $= 1·3 \times 10^{13}$ mol⁻⁴ l⁴ and K_{stab} for the copper(II)–EDTA complex $= 6·3 \times 10^{18}$ mol⁻¹ l).

(b) Add an equal volume of hydrochloric acid–sodium acetate buffer solution (pH 2)* to a few drops of 0·1 M iron(III) chloride solution diluted to 5 cm³ with water. Add 0·1 M potassium thiocyanate solution to produce a deep red solution:

$$Fe^{3+} + SCN^- \rightleftharpoons [FeSCN]^{2+}$$

and add the EDTA solution to this gradually with thorough mixing. Note any colour change which occurs and suggest an explanation for this observation (K_{stab} for the $[FeSCN]^{2+}$ complex $= 1·4 \times 10^2$ mol⁻¹ l and K_{stab} for the iron(III)–EDTA complex $= 1·2 \times 10^{25}$ mol⁻¹ l).

(c) Add an equal volume of ammonia–ammonium chloride buffer solution (pH 10)* to a few drops of 0·1 M magnesium sulphate solution diluted to 5 cm³ and add sufficient Eriochrome Black T indicator* to give a red colour. Add the EDTA solution slowly with shaking until no further change occurs and explain any colour change which occurs (K_{stab} for the magnesium–indicator complex $= 1 \times 10^7$ mol⁻¹ l and K_{stab} for the magnesium–EDTA complex $= 4·9 \times 10^8$ mol⁻¹ l).

2. Determination of the percentage of zinc in hydrated zinc sulphate

Weigh out accurately about 7 g of zinc sulphate crystals, dissolve in distilled water and dilute to exactly 250 cm³. Pipette 25 cm³ of this

*See Appendix II.

solution into a conical flask, dilute to 100 cm^3 with distilled water and add 2 cm^3 of ammonia–ammonium chloride buffer solution (pH 10) and enough solid Eriochrome Black T indicator* to give a clearly visible colour. Titrate with the standard EDTA solution (0·1 M) until the colour changes from red to blue.

The equation for the reaction is essentially:

$$Zn^{2+} + Y^{4-} \rightarrow ZnY^{2-}$$

$$\therefore (MV)_{Zn^{2+}} = (MV)_{EDTA}$$

Calculate the concentration of Zn^{2+} in g l^{-1} and hence the percentage of zinc in the sample.

3. Determination of the percentage of magnesium in hydrated magnesium sulphate

Proceed as in experiment (2) using about 6 g of a dried sample of magnesium sulphate crystals. Complex formation is relatively slow at room temperature so the EDTA should be added slowly near the end-point. Alternatively, the solution in the conical flask may be heated to approximately 40 °C.

The equation for the reaction is essentially:

$$Mg^{2+} + Y^{4-} \rightarrow MgY^{2-}$$

$$\therefore (MV)_{Mg^{2+}} = (MV)_{EDTA}$$

Calculate the concentration of Mg^{2+} in g l^{-1} and hence the percentage of magnesium in the sample.

4. Determination of the total hardness of water

Hardness in water is caused by dissolved calcium and magnesium salts. It may be expressed as parts of $CaCO_3$ per million parts of water.

Pipette 100 cm^3 of the sample of water into a conical flask and add 2 cm^3 of ammonia–ammonium chloride buffer solution (pH 10) and enough solid Eriochrome Black T indicator* to give a definite colour. Titrate with the standard EDTA solution (0·1 M) until the colour changes from red to blue. Calculate the total hardness of the water.

To determine the *permanent hardness* of the sample proceed as follows. Pipette 100 cm^3 of the sample of water into a 250 cm^3 beaker and boil gently for about 30 minutes. This removes the *temporary hardness* from the water, e.g.

$$Ca(HCO_3)_2 \rightarrow CaCO_3(s) + CO_2(g) + H_2O$$

Cool and filter into a 100 cm^3 graduated flask, making up to the mark with distilled water. Mix thoroughly. Titrate the filtrate as before and

*See Appendix II.

calculate the permanent hardness of the water and hence the temporary hardness by subtracting the permanent from the total hardness.

5. Determination of the purity of a nickel(II) salt by back titration

Note. Nickel(II) cannot be titrated directly with EDTA using Erio-chrome Black T as indicator as the nickel(II)-indicator complex is more stable than the nickel(II)-EDTA complex.

Weigh out accurately about 6 g of pure nickel(II) chloride, dissolve it in distilled water and dilute to exactly 250 cm³. Pipette 25 cm³ of this solution into a conical flask and add a known excess of standard EDTA solution (0·1 M) from a burette (about 35 cm³ will be sufficient). Dilute the solution to about 200 cm³ and add 4 cm³ of ammonia–ammonium chloride buffer solution (pH 10) and enough solid Eriochrome Black T indicator* to give a definite colour. Titrate the excess of EDTA with standard 0·1 M zinc sulphate solution (made by dissolving 7·19 g of 'Analar' zinc sulphate in distilled water and diluting to exactly 250 cm³) until the colour changes from red to blue.

The equations for the reactions involved are:

$$Ni^{2+} + Y^{4-} \rightarrow NiY^{2-}$$

and,
$$Zn^{2+} + Y^{4-} \rightarrow ZnY^{2-}$$

$$\therefore (MV)_{\text{EDTA (excess)}} = (MV)_{Zn^{2+}}$$

Hence calculate the volume of EDTA solution which has reacted with the nickel(II) chloride solution and using the relationship

$$(MV)_{Ni^{2+}} = (MV)_{\text{EDTA}}$$

calculate the percentage purity of the nickel(II) chloride.

For further reading

1. E. E. Aynsley and A. B. Littlewood, *Principles of Titrimetric Analysis,* pp. 23–30. The Royal Institute of Chemistry, 1962.
2. G. F. Condike, 'Complexometric Titrations of Heavy Metals', *Chemistry*, 1966, 6, **39**, 28–32.
3. H. Flaschka, *EDTA Titrations*. Pergamon Press, 1959.
4. A. I. Vogel, *A Textbook of Quantitative Inorganic Analysis* (Third Edition), Chapter 4. Longmans, 1962.
   Complexometric (largely EDTA) titrations: theory, metal ion indicators and applications.
5. T. S. West and A. S. Sykes, *Analytical Applications of Diamino-Ethane-Tetra-Acetic Acid* (Second Edition). The British Drug Houses Ltd, 1960.

*See Appendix II.

6 Conductometric and Potentiometric Titrations

In some cases the stoichiometric point of a titration reaction cannot be found by means of a chemical indicator because (*a*) no suitable indicator is available, (*b*) the end-point is not sharp enough, or (*c*) the titration mixture is highly coloured or turbid. The end-point in these cases must be determined by using other properties such as the change in conductivity or e.m.f. which is sharp at the stoichiometric point. These methods are accurate, even when dilute solutions are used, and they can be used for acid-base, redox and precipitation titrations. A titration in which the end-point is determined by means of a change in conductivity is known as a *conductometric titration* and one in which the end-point is detected by means of a change in e.m.f. is known as a *potentiometric titration*.

Conductometric Titrations

In the titration of a strong acid with a strong base, e.g. hydrochloric acid with sodium hydroxide, the reaction involved can be represented by the equation:

$$H^+(aq) + OH^-(aq) \rightarrow H_2O$$

sodium (Na^+) and chloride (Cl^-) ions also being present. As the sodium hydroxide is added to the acid, the highly mobile hydrogen ions are replaced by the sodium ions which have a much lower conductivity. There is, therefore, an initial decrease in conductivity, which reaches a minimum at the stoichiometric point. The conductivity subsequently increases again if the addition of sodium hydroxide is continued, as the conductivity of the hydroxide ions is high. If the conductivity of the solution is plotted against the volume of base added, a curve of the type shown in Fig. 6.1 is obtained, the minimum in the conductivity being taken as the end-point.

The curve obtained for the titration of a weak acid, e.g. acetic acid, with a strong base is shown in Fig. 6.2. The initial conductivity is low as the weak acid is only slightly dissociated:

$$CH_3COOH \rightleftharpoons H^+ + CH_3COO^-$$

As the base is added, the conductivity falls slightly as hydrogen ions are removed. The conductivity then increases gradually as the weak acid is converted to its sodium salt which is a strong electrolyte ($CH_3COO^-Na^+$). At the stoichiometric point the conductivity increases much more rapidly due to the addition of an excess of hydroxide ions.

In a precipitation titration, such as that in which sodium chloride

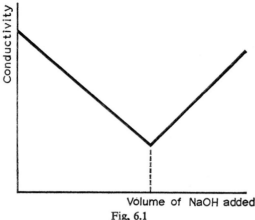

Fig. 6.1

solution is titrated with silver nitrate solution, the equation for the reaction involved is:

$$Ag^+(aq) + Cl^-(aq) \rightarrow AgCl(s)$$

in the presence of sodium (Na^+) and nitrate (NO_3^-) ions. The conductivity falls slightly up to the stoichiometric point, as the conductivity of the sodium ions is slightly less than that of the silver ions, which are removed from solution as a precipitate of silver chloride (the chloride and nitrate ions have similar conductivities). Subsequently, the conductivity rises due to the addition of further sodium and chloride ions beyond the stoichiometric point (Fig. 6.3).

1. **Conductometric titration of sodium hydroxide solution with hydrochloric acid**

Immerse a dip-type conductivity cell in a beaker containing 50 cm³ of standard hydrochloric acid (about 0·01 M). Connect the electrodes to the conductivity bridge as shown in Fig. 6.4.* Adjust the variable resistance (R_2) to give a null point (minimum sound in the headphones) near the centre of the slide-wire. Alternating current supplied by an induction coil or a valve oscillator is used to avoid polarisation effects. At the balance point:

$$\frac{R_1}{R_2} = \frac{AB}{BC}$$

and the conductivity of the solution $= \dfrac{1}{R_1}.$

Now stir the solution continuously while adding the sodium hydroxide solution (about 0·1 M) 0·5 cm³ at a time from a 10 cm³ micro-burette.

*Alternatively, a conductivity bridge such as the Grayshaw CT50 may be used if available.

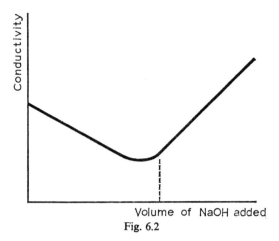

Fig. 6.2

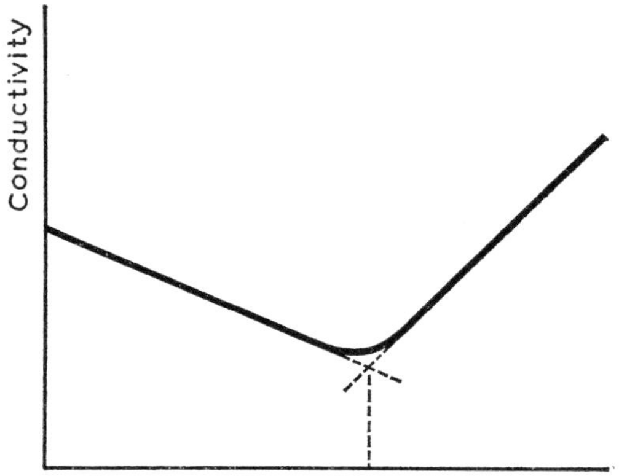

Fig. 6.3

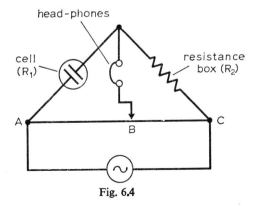

Fig. 6.4

E

Measure the conductivity of the solution after each addition and record the burette readings and corresponding conductivities. The titration should be continued well beyond the stoichiometric point. Plot a graph of conductivity against volume of sodium hydroxide added and draw two straight lines through the points to obtain the end-point. Calculate the exact molarity of the sodium hydroxide solution.

2. Conductometric titration of sodium hydroxide solution with acetic acid

Repeat experiment (1) using 50 cm³ of approximately 0·1 M acetic acid and 1 M sodium hydroxide solution. Calculate the exact molarity of the acetic acid.

3. Conductometric titration of sodium chloride solution with silver nitrate solution

The procedure is exactly the same as in experiment (1) and the graph obtained is of the form shown in Fig. 6.3. Use 50 cm³ of 0·01 M sodium chloride solution and approximately 0·1 M silver nitrate solution.

Potentiometric Titrations

The end-point of an acid-base titration may be determined by direct measurement of the change in pH of the solution as the reagent is added from the burette. A pH meter, which employs a cell consisting of a *reference* electrode (unaffected by change in pH) and a glass *indicator* electrode (sensitive to change in pH), is used for this purpose. A pH meter is essentially a valve voltmeter (the resistance of a glass electrode is very high) which can be calibrated in a buffer solution of known pH. A rapid change in pH occurs at the stoichiometric point and the end-point is taken as the point at which the rate of change of pH is a maximum (Fig. 6.5). A more accurate end-point may be obtained by plotting a graph of $\dfrac{\Delta(\text{pH})}{\Delta V}$, where $\Delta(\text{pH})$ is the change in pH corresponding to the addition of a *small* volume ΔV of reagent from the burette, against the volume of reagent added from the burette in the region of the end-point. There is a maximum in the latter curve as shown in Fig. 6.6.

Redox and precipitation titrations may also be carried out by measuring the change in e.m.f. of a cell consisting of a reference electrode and a suitable indicator electrode. A platinum electrode may be used as the indicator electrode in a redox titration and a silver electrode in a silver nitrate precipitation titration. This *potentiometric* method, in which the end-point of a titration is detected by the measurement of e.m.f., is widely used in industry and instruments which carry out potentiometric

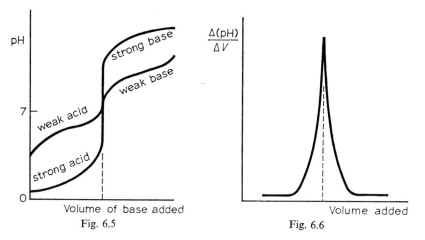

Fig. 6.5   Fig. 6.6

titrations automatically are now available. A rapid change in e.m.f. occurs at the stoichiometric point and the curve obtained by plotting the e.m.f. of the cell against the volume of reagent added from the burette may be almost vertical at this point, although in other cases the change may be more gradual.

A typical experimental arrangement for a potentiometric titration is shown in Fig. 6.7. A dip-type calomel electrode, consisting of mercury in contact with a layer of calomel (Hg_2Cl_2) and a saturated solution of potassium chloride, is often used as the reference electrode and this is combined with a suitable indicator electrode to form a complete cell. The pH (or e.m.f.) of this cell is measured as various amounts of the solution in the burette are added and the end-point of the titration is obtained by plotting a graph by pH (or e.m.f.) against volume of

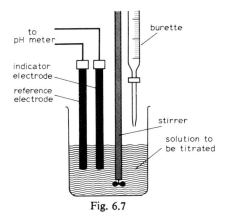

Fig. 6.7

solution added from the burette. The following practical points should always be carefully observed.

(*a*) The pH meter should be set up in accordance with the manufacturer's instructions. *It is an expensive instrument and should not be used until the correct technique for using it is fully understood.*

(*b*) The electrodes are fragile and should always be handled with great care. They should be washed thoroughly with distilled water before use and dried carefully with filter paper. They must be below the surface of the solution to be titrated.

(*c*) A stirrer should be placed in the solution in the beaker to ensure thorough mixing with the solution added from the burette.

(*d*) The pH (or e.m.f.) should be determined after each addition of solution from the burette, allowing sufficient time for the potential of the indicator electrode to reach a reasonably steady value.

(*e*) A preliminary titration may be carried out to determine the region where the pH (or e.m.f.) changes most rapidly. The titration is then repeated, making more measurements in this region.

1. Potentiometric titration of hydrochloric acid with sodium hydroxide solution

A glass indicator electrode and a calomel reference electrode are used in this titration. Initially the pH of the solution increases as the hydrogen ions of the acid are neutralised by the hydroxide ions of the sodium hydroxide added from the burette:

$$H^+(aq) + OH^-(aq) \rightarrow H_2O \tag{1}$$

and the pH increases further beyond the stoichiometric point due to the excess of hydroxide ions. The end-point will occur at approximately pH 7. The change in pH at the end-point is very sharp.

Calibrate the pH meter using two buffer solutions of appreciably different pH, e.g. 0·05 M potassium hydrogen phthalate solution (pH = 4·00 at 20 °C) and 0·01 M borax (pH = 9·18 at 20 °C), by immersing the glass electrode and the calomel electrode in the buffer solution of known pH.

Pipette 25 cm³ of standard hydrochloric acid (about 0·1 M) into a 250 cm³ beaker and immerse the electrodes in the solution. Distilled water should be added if necessary so that the tips of the electrodes are below the surface of the solution. Switch on the stirrer and set the pH meter to the 0–8 pH range (change to the 6–14 range when pH 6 is reached). Fill the burette with approximately 0·1 M sodium hydroxide solution. Read the pH meter before any sodium hydroxide is added and then add 2 cm³ of sodium hydroxide solution, recording the pH of the solution after allowing sufficient time for the pH meter reading to reach a steady value. Continue to make 2 cm³ additions in this way, recording the pH after each addition, until the end-point is approached when

0·1 cm³ additions of sodium hydroxide should be made. The titration should be continued beyond the end-point, increasing to 2 cm³ additions when the pH begins to increase more slowly again.

The titration may be repeated using 25 cm³ of standard acetic acid (about 0·1 M) in place of the hydrochloric acid.

Plot a graph of pH against volume of sodium hydroxide added in each titration and determine from the graph the volume of sodium hydroxide corresponding to the end-point. To obtain a more accurate end-point plot a graph of $\dfrac{\Delta(\mathrm{pH})}{\Delta V}$ against volume of sodium hydroxide added in the region of the end-point. The volume of sodium hydroxide corresponding to the maximum in the latter curve is taken as the end-point.

Calculate the molarity of the sodium hydroxide solution using:

$$(MV)_{\text{base}} = (MV)_{\text{acid}}$$

a relation which follows from equation (1).

2. Potentiometric titration of ammonium iron(II) sulphate solution with potassium dichromate solution

Pipette 25 cm³ of approximately 0·1 M ammonium iron(II) sulphate solution into a 250 cm³ beaker and add about 25 cm³ of dilute sulphuric acid. Immerse a bright platinum indicator electrode (cleaned with chromic acid and washed with water before use) and a calomel reference electrode in the solution and use the pH meter directly on the millivolt scale. Titrate with standard potassium dichromate solution (about 0·02 M) in the burette as described in experiment (1), with the pH meter switched to the 0–800 mV range initially. The change in e.m.f. is due to the change in oxidation number of the manganese from +7 to +2 and of the iron from +2 to +3:

$$6\mathrm{Fe^{2+}} + \mathrm{Cr_2O_7^{2-}} + 14\mathrm{H^+} \rightarrow 6\mathrm{Fe^{3+}} + 2\mathrm{Cr^{3+}} + 7\mathrm{H_2O} \qquad (2)$$

Plot a graph of

(a) e.m.f. against volume of potassium dichromate added, and

(b) $\dfrac{\Delta E}{\Delta V}$, where ΔE is the change in e.m.f. corresponding to the addition of a *small* volume ΔV of potassium dichromate, against volume of potassium dichromate added in the region of the end-point.

Hence determine the end-point for the titration.

Calculate the molarity of the ammonium iron(II) sulphate solution using:

$$(MV)_{\mathrm{Fe^{2+}}} = 6(MV)_{\mathrm{Cr_2O_7^{2-}}}$$

a relation which follows from equation (2).

3. Potentiometric titration of silver nitrate solution with sodium chloride solution

Pipette 25 cm³ of approximately 0·1 M silver nitrate solution into a 250 cm³ beaker. Immerse a silver electrode (cleaned in a little 1:1 nitric acid and washed with distilled water before use) and a calomel reference electrode in the solution* and use the pH meter directly on the millivolt scale. Titrate with standard sodium chloride solution (about 0·1 M) in the burette as described in experiment (1), with the pH meter switched to the 0–800 mV range. The change in e.m.f. is due to the removal of silver ions from the solution:

$$Ag^+(aq) + Cl^-(aq) \rightarrow AgCl(s) \tag{3}$$

The readings may tend to fluctuate due to the presence of the silver chloride precipitate and the stirrer should be switched off if necessary to allow the precipitate to settle before taking a reading.

Plot a graph of

(a) e.m.f. against volume of sodium chloride added, and

(b) $\dfrac{\Delta E}{\Delta V}$, where ΔE is the change in e.m.f. corresponding to the addition of a *small* volume ΔV of sodium chloride, against volume of sodium chloride added in the region of the end-point.

Hence determine the end-point for the titration.

Calculate the molarity of the silver nitrate solution using:

$$(MV)_{Ag^+} = (MV)_{Cl^-}$$

a relation which follows from equation (3).

For further reading

1. L. C. Roselaar, *Systematic Physical Chemistry*, Chapters 10 and 11. John Murray, 1975.
   The ionic theory and conductivity.
2. A. I. Vogel, *A Textbook of Quantitative Inorganic Analysis* (Third Edition), Chapter 17. Longmans, 1962.
   Conductometric titrations: theory, apparatus and applications.
3. D. Chamberlain, 'Potentiometric Titrations', *The School Science Review*, 1960, 146, **42**, 115–127.
4. A. I. Vogel, reference (2), Chapter 16.
   Potentiometric titrations: theory, apparatus and applications.

* For accurate results the calomel electrode should be immersed in a beaker containing saturated potassium chloride solution and separated from the silver nitrate solution by means of a salt bridge of saturated potassium nitrate solution.

Appendix I Atomic Weights

The values given in the table below are based on $^{12}C = 12$

Element	Atomic number	Atomic weight	Element	Atomic number	Atomic weight
Al Aluminium	13	26·98	Li Lithium	3	6·94
Sb Antimony	51	121·75	Mg Magnesium	12	24·30
As Arsenic	33	74·92	Mn Manganese	25	54·94
Ba Barium	56	137·34	Hg Mercury	80	200·59
Bi Bismuth	83	208·98	Mo Molybdenum	42	95·94
B Boron	5	10·81	Ni Nickel	28	58·71
Br Bromine	35	79·90	N Nitrogen	7	14·007
Cd Cadmium	48	112·40	O Oxygen	8	15·999
Ca Calcium	20	40·08	P Phosphorus	15	30·97
C Carbon	6	12·01	K Potassium	19	39·10
Ce Cerium	58	140·12	Si Silicon	14	28·09
Cl Chlorine	17	35·45	Ag Silver	47	107·87
Cr Chromium	24	52·00	Na Sodium	11	22·99
Co Cobalt	27	58·93	Sr Strontium	38	87·62
Cu Copper	29	63·55	S Sulphur	16	32·06
F Fluorine	9	19·00	Sn Tin	50	118·69
H Hydrogen	1	1·008	Ti Titanium	22	47·90
I Iodine	53	126·90	U Uranium	92	238·03
Fe Iron	26	55·85	V Vanadium	23	50·94
Pb Lead	82	207·2	Zn Zinc	30	65·37

Appendix II Tabulated Data on Titrimetric Reagents

1. Molecular weights of standard substances

Type of titration	Substance	Molecular weight
Acid-base	Borax, $Na_2B_4O_7.10H_2O$	381·37
	Sodium carbonate, Na_2CO_3	105·99
	Hydrochloric acid, HCl	36·46
	Sulphamic acid, NH_2SO_3H	97·09
Redox	Sodium oxalate, $Na_2C_2O_4$	134·00
	Arsenic(III) oxide, As_2O_3	197·84
	Potassium dichromate, $K_2Cr_2O_7$	294·19
	Potassium iodate, KIO_3	214·00
	Iodine, I_2	253·81
Precipitation	Sodium chloride, NaCl	58·44
Complexometric	Disodium salt of EDTA, $Na_2H_2C_{10}H_{12}O_8N_2.2H_2O$	372·24

2. Indicators

(a) Acid-base indicators

Indicator	pH range	Colour change acid-alkali	Preparation of solution
Methyl orange*	3·1–4·4	red-yellow	0·1% in water
Methyl red	4·4–6·2	red-yellow	0·1% in water
Phenolphthalein	8·3–10·0	colourless-red	0·5% in 50% ethanol

*Screened methyl orange (colour change: red-green) is prepared by dissolving 1·0 g of methyl orange and 1·4 g of xylene cyanol FF in 500 cm³ of 50 per cent ethanol.

(b) *Redox indicators*

Indicator	Potential at colour change/V	Colour change oxidised-reduced form	Preparation of solution
Barium diphenylamine p-sulphonate	+0·84	violet-colour-less	0·2% in water
Starch, $I_2.I^-$	+0·54	deep blue-colourless	Make 2 g of soluble starch and 0·01 g of $HgCl_2$ into a thin paste with water. Add slowly to 1 l of boiling water with constant stirring. Boil for a few minutes and cool

(c) *Precipitation indicators*

Indicator	Colour change at end-point	Preparation of solution	Use
Potassium chromate	Appearance of faint red tinge	5% in water	Cl^- or Br^- with Ag^+ in neutral solution
Fluorescein	Yellow-green solution → pink precipitate	0·2% (Na salt) in water	Cl^-, Br^- or I^- with Ag^+ in neutral or faintly acidic solution
Dichloro-fluorescein	Yellow-green solution → red precipitate	0·1% (Na salt) in water	Cl^-, Br^- or I^- with Ag^+ in pH range 4·4–7
Ammonium iron(III) alum	Appearance of faint red tinge	Saturated solution in the presence of dil. HNO_3	SCN^- with Ag^+

(d) *Complexometric indicator*
Eriochrome Black T (colour change: red-blue) is prepared by grinding together 0·1 g of the solid and 10 g of 'Analar' sodium chloride. It should be kept in a stoppered bottle.

3. Preparation of buffer solutions

(a) *Hydrochloric acid–sodium acetate buffer* (pH 2)
Mix 21·0 cm³ of 1 M hydrochloric acid and 20·0 cm³ of 1 M sodium acetate solution and dilute to 100 cm³.

(b) *Ammonia–ammonium chloride buffer* (pH 10)
Dissolve 6·75 g of ammonium chloride in 57·0 cm³ of 0·880 ammonia solution and dilute to 100 cm³.
Note. 'Analar' reagents should be used.

4. Preparation of zinc amalgam

Note. Mercury vapour is highly poisonous. The preparation should, therefore, be carried out in a fume cupboard.

Place 20 cm³ (270 g) of mercury in a beaker and cover it with about 5 cm³ of 1 : 4 concentrated sulphuric acid/water. Add 12 g of granulated zinc and warm gently, when the zinc dissolves in the mercury to form a liquid amalgam. If some solid amalgam is also present after a few minutes' heating add a little more mercury. Allow to cool before use.

5. Standard redox potentials $E^{\ominus}$ at 25 °C

Half-reaction	$E^{\ominus}/V$	Half-reaction	$E^{\ominus}/V$
$H_3AsO_4 + 2H^+ + 2e^- = H_3AsO_3 + H_2O$	+0·56	$I_2 + 2e^- = 2I^-$	+0·54
$Br_2 + 2e^- = 2Br^-$	+1·07	$IO_3^- + 6H^+ + 5e^- = \frac{1}{2}I_2 + 3H_2O$	+1·19
$2CO_2 + 2H^+ + 2e^- = H_2C_2O_4$	−0·49	$MnO_4^- + 8H^+ + 5e^- = Mn^{2+} + 4H_2O$	+1·52
$Cl_2 + 2e^- = 2Cl^-$	+1·36	$O_2 + 2H^+ + 2e^- = H_2O_2$	+0·68
$HClO + H^+ + 2e^- = Cl^- + H_2O$	+1·49	$SO_4^{2-} + 4H^+ + 2e^- = H_2SO_3 + H_2O$	+0·17
$Cr_2O_7^{2-} + 14H^+ + 6e^- = 2Cr^{3+} + 7H_2O$	+1·33	$S_4O_6^{2-} + 2e^- = 2S_2O_3^{2-}$	+0·09
$Cu^{2+} + I^- + e^- = CuI$	+0·86	$Sn^{4+} + 2e^- = Sn^{2+}$	+0·15
$Fe^{3+} + e^- = Fe^{2+}$	+0·77	$V^{3+} + e^- = V^{2+}$	−0·26
$[Fe(CN)_6]^{3-} + e^- = [Fe(CN)_6]^{4-}$	+0·36	$VO^{2+} + 2H^+ + e^- = V^{3+} + H_2O$	+0·34
$2Hg^{2+} + 2e^- = Hg_2^{2+}$	+0·91	$VO_2^+ + 2H^+ + e^- = VO^{2+} + H_2O$	+1·00

Note. The values of $E^{\ominus}$ are referred to the potential of the standard hydrogen electrode taken as zero. A reaction which proceeds to the right more readily than the reaction
$$2H^+ + 2e^- = H_2$$
under standard conditions is given a positive potential and one which proceeds less readily is given a negative potential.

Appendix III Chemical Nomenclature

In 1972 the Association for Science Education (A.S.E.) published a report entitled *Chemical Nomenclature, Symbols and Terminology* and a new edition of this report appeared in 1979. Following the publication of the A.S.E. report the G.C.E. Boards issued a joint statement on chemical nomenclature listing the general principles which they would adopt in setting examination papers. The nomenclature in this book is generally in line with these recommendations as far as compounds of metals are concerned, but in other compounds there are differences. The table below shows the common current names (in alphabetical order) for a number of substances mentioned in this book with the corresponding recommended names.

(a) Inorganic

Common current name	Recommended name
arsenite	arsenate(III)
borax	disodium tetraborate-10-water
chlorate	chlorate(V)
chromate	chromate(VI)
chromic acid	chromic(VI) acid
dichromate	dichromate(VI)
ethylenediamine tetra-acetic acid, disodium salt (EDTA)	bis[di(carboxymethyl)-amino]ethane, disodium salt (edta)
hypochlorite	chlorate(I)
iodate	iodate(V)
manganate	manganate(VI)
manganese dioxide	manganese(IV) oxide
metavanadate	polytrioxovanadate(V)
nitric acid/nitrate	nitric(V) acid/nitrate(V)
permanganate	manganate(VII)
(ortho)phosphoric acid	phosphoric(V) acid
sulphamic acid	aminosulphonic acid
sulphuric acid/sulphate	sulphuric(VI) acid/sulphate(VI)
sulphite	sulphate(IV)
thiosulphate	thiosulphate(VI)

(b) Organic

Common current name	Recommended name
acetic acid/acetate	ethanoic acid/ethanoate
chloroform	trichloromethane
formaldehyde	methanal
formate	methanoate
oxalic acid/oxalate	ethanedioic acid/ethanedioate

LOGARITHMS OF NUMBERS

	0	1	2	3	4	5	6	7	8	9	Differences 1 2 3	4 5 6	7 8 9
10	·0000	0043	0086	0128	0170	0212					4 8 13	17 21 25	29 34 38
						0212	0253	0294	0334	0374	4 8 12	16 20 24	28 32 36
11	·0414	0453	0492	0531	0569	0607					4 8 12	16 19 23	27 31 35
						0607	0645	0682	0719	0755	4 7 11	15 18 22	26 30 33
12	·0792	0828	0864	0899	0934	0969					4 7 11	14 18 21	25 28 32
						0969	1004	1038	1072	1106	3 7 10	14 17 20	24 27 31
13	·1139	1173	1206	1239	1271	1303					3 7 10	13 16 20	23 26 30
						1303	1335	1367	1399	1430	3 6 10	13 16 19	22 26 29
14	·1461	1492	1523	1553	1584	1614	1644	1673	1703	1732	3 6 9	12 15 18	21 24 27
15	·1761	1790	1818	1847	1875	1903	1931	1959	1987	2014	3 6 8	11 14 17	20 22 25
16	·2041	2068	2095	2122	2148	2175	2201	2227	2253	2279	3 5 8	10 13 16	18 21 23
17	·2304	2330	2355	2380	2405	2430	2455	2480	2504	2529	2 5 7	10 12 15	17 20 22
18	·2553	2577	2601	2625	2648	2672	2695	2718	2742	2765	2 5 7	9 12 14	16 19 21
19	·2788	2810	2833	2856	2878	2900	2923	2945	2967	2989	2 4 7	9 11 13	15 18 20
20	·3010	3032	3054	3075	3096	3118	3139	3160	3181	3201	2 4 6	8 11 13	15 17 19
21	·3222	3243	3263	3284	3304	3324	3345	3365	3385	3404	2 4 6	8 10 12	14 16 18
22	·3424	3444	3464	3483	3502	3522	3541	3560	3579	3598	2 4 6	8 10 11	13 15 17
23	·3617	3636	3655	3674	3692	3711	3729	3747	3766	3784	2 4 6	7 9 11	13 15 17
24	·3802	3820	3838	3856	3874	3892	3909	3927	3945	3962	2 4 5	7 9 11	13 14 16
25	·3979	3997	4014	4031	4048	4065	4082	4099	4116	4133	2 3 5	7 9 10	12 14 15
26	·4150	4166	4183	4200	4216	4232	4249	4265	4281	4298	2 3 5	6 8 10	11 13 14
27	·4314	4330	4346	4362	4378	4393	4409	4425	4440	4456	2 3 5	6 8 9	11 13 14
28	·4472	4487	4502	4518	4533	4548	4564	4579	4594	4609	2 3 5	6 8 9	11 12 14
29	·4624	4639	4654	4669	4683	4698	4713	4728	4742	4757	1 3 4	6 7 9	10 12 13
30	·4771	4786	4800	4814	4829	4843	4857	4871	4886	4900	1 3 4	6 7 8	10 11 13
31	·4914	4928	4942	4955	4969	4983	4997	5011	5024	5038	1 3 4	5 7 8	10 11 12
32	·5051	5065	5079	5092	5105	5119	5132	5145	5159	5172	1 3 4	5 7 8	9 11 12
33	·5185	5198	5211	5224	5237	5250	5263	5276	5289	5302	1 3 4	5 7 8	9 10 12
34	·5315	5328	5340	5353	5366	5378	5391	5403	5416	5428	1 3 4	5 6 8	9 10 11
35	·5441	5453	5465	5478	5490	5502	5514	5527	5539	5551	1 2 4	5 6 7	8 10 11
36	·5563	5575	5587	5599	5611	5623	5635	5647	5658	5670	1 2 4	5 6 7	8 10 11
37	·5682	5694	5705	5717	5729	5740	5752	5763	5775	5786	1 2 3	5 6 7	8 9 10
38	·5798	5809	5821	5832	5843	5855	5866	5877	5888	5899	1 2 3	5 6 7	8 9 10
39	·5911	5922	5933	5944	5955	5966	5977	5988	5999	6010	1 2 3	4 6 7	8 9 10
40	·6021	6031	6042	6053	6064	6075	6085	6096	6107	6117	1 2 3	4 5 6	7 9 10
41	·6128	6138	6149	6160	6170	6180	6191	6201	6212	6222	1 2 3	4 5 6	7 8 9
42	·6232	6243	6253	6263	6274	6284	6294	6304	6314	6325	1 2 3	4 5 6	7 8 9
43	·6335	6345	6355	6365	6375	6385	6395	6405	6415	6425	1 2 3	4 5 6	7 8 9
44	·6435	6444	6454	6464	6474	6484	6493	6503	6513	6522	1 2 3	4 5 6	7 8 9
45	·6532	6542	6551	6561	6571	6580	6590	6599	6609	6618	1 2 3	4 5 6	7 8 9
46	·6628	6637	6646	6656	6665	6675	6684	6693	6702	6712	1 2 3	4 5 6	7 7 8
47	·6721	6730	6739	6749	6758	6767	6776	6785	6794	6803	1 2 3	4 5 5	6 7 8
48	·6812	6821	6830	6839	6848	6857	6866	6875	6884	6893	1 2 3	4 5 5	6 7 8
49	·6902	6911	6920	6928	6937	6946	6955	6964	6972	6981	1 2 3	4 4 5	6 7 8

The logarithm tables are adapted and reproduced from Knott's *Four Figure Mathematical Tables,* by permission of the publishers, Messrs. W. and R. Chambers Ltd.

LOGARITHMS OF NUMBERS

	0	1	2	3	4	5	6	7	8	9	1 2 3	4 5 6	7 8 9
												Differences	
50	·6990	6998 7007 7016			7024 7033 7042			7050 7059 7067			1 2 3	3 4 5	6 7 8
51	·7076	7084 7093 7101			7110 7118 7126			7135 7143 7152			1 2 3	3 4 5	6 7 8
52	·7160	7168 7177 7185			7193 7202 7210			7218 7226 7235			1 2 2	3 4 5	6 7 7
53	·7243	7251 7259 7267			7275 7284 7292			7300 7308 7316			1 2 2	3 4 5	6 6 7
54	·7324	7332 7340 7348			7356 7364 7372			7380 7388 7396			1 2 2	3 4 5	6 6 7
55	·7404	7412 7419 7427			7435 7443 7451			7459 7466 7474			1 2 2	3 4 5	5 6 7
56	·7482	7490 7497 7505			7513 7520 7528			7536 7543 7551			1 2 2	3 4 5	5 6 7
57	·7559	7566 7574 7582			7589 7597 7604			7612 7619 7627			1 2 2	3 4 5	5 6 7
58	·7634	7642 7649 7657			7664 7672 7679			7686 7694 7701			1 2 2	3 4 4	5 6 7
59	·7709	7716 7723 7731			7738 7745 7752			7760 7767 7774			1 1 2	3 4 4	5 6 7
60	·7782	7789 7796 7803			7810 7818 7825			7832 7839 7846			1 1 2	3 4 4	5 6 6
61	·7853	7860 7868 7875			7882 7889 7896			7903 7910 7917			1 1 2	3 4 4	5 6 6
62	·7924	7931 7938 7945			7952 7959 7966			7973 7980 7987			1 1 2	3 3 4	5 6 6
63	·7993	8000 8007 8014			8021 8028 8035			8041 8048 8055			1 1 2	3 3 4	5 6 6
64	·8062	8069 8075 8082			8089 8096 8102			8109 8116 8122			1 1 2	3 3 4	5 5 6
65	·8129	8136 8142 8149			8156 8162 8169			8176 8182 8189			1 1 2	3 3 4	5 5 6
66	·8195	8202 8209 8215			8222 8228 8235			8241 8248 8254			1 1 2	3 3 4	5 5 6
67	·8261	8267 8274 8280			8287 8293 8299			8306 8312 8319			1 1 2	3 3 4	4 5 6
68	·8325	8331 8338 8344			8351 8357 8363			8370 8376 8382			1 1 2	3 3 4	4 5 6
69	·8388	8395 8401 8407			8414 8420 8426			8432 8439 8445			1 1 2	3 3 4	4 5 6
70	·8451	8457 8463 8470			8476 8482 8488			8494 8500 8506			1 1 2	2 3 4	4 5 6
71	·8513	8519 8525 8531			8537 8543 8549			8555 8561 8567			1 1 2	2 3 4	4 5 5
72	·8573	8579 8585 8591			8597 8603 8609			8615 8621 8627			1 1 2	2 3 4	4 5 5
73	·8633	8639 8645 8651			8657 8663 8669			8675 8681 8686			1 1 2	2 3 4	4 5 5
74	·8692	8698 8704 8710			8716 8722 8727			8733 8739 8745			1 1 2	2 3 4	4 5 5
75	·8751	8756 8762 8768			8774 8779 8785			8791 8797 8802			1 1 2	2 3 3	4 5 5
76	·8808	8814 8820 8825			8831 8837 8842			8848 8854 8859			1 1 2	2 3 3	4 5 5
77	·8865	8871 8876 8882			8887 8893 8899			8904 8910 8915			1 1 2	2 3 3	4 4 5
78	·8921	8927 8932 8938			8943 8949 8954			8960 8965 8971			1 1 2	2 3 3	4 4 5
79	·8976	8982 8987 8993			8998 9004 9009			9015 9020 9025			1 1 2	2 3 3	4 4 5
80	·9031	9036 9042 9047			9053 9058 9063			9069 9074 9079			1 1 2	2 3 3	4 4 5
81	·9085	9090 9096 9101			9106 9112 9117			9122 9128 9133			1 1 2	2 3 3	4 4 5
82	·9138	9143 9149 9154			9159 9165 9170			9175 9180 9186			1 1 2	2 3 3	4 4 5
83	·9191	9196 9201 9206			9212 9217 9222			9227 9232 9238			1 1 2	2 3 3	4 4 5
84	·9243	9248 9253 9258			9263 9269 9274			9279 9284 9289			1 1 2	2 3 3	4 4 5
85	·9294	9299 9304 9309			9315 9320 9325			9330 9335 9340			1 1 2	2 3 3	4 4 5
86	·9345	9350 9355 9360			9365 9370 9375			9380 9385 9390			1 1 2	2 3 3	4 4 5
87	·9395	9400 9405 9410			9415 9420 9425			9430 9435 9440			0 1 1	2 2 3	3 4 4
88	·9445	9450 9455 9460			9465 9469 9474			9479 9484 9489			0 1 1	2 2 3	3 4 4
89	·9494	9499 9504 9509			9513 9518 9523			9528 9533 9538			0 1 1	2 2 3	3 4 4
90	·9542	9547 9552 9557			9562 9566 9571			9576 9581 9586			0 1 1	2 2 3	3 4 4
91	·9590	9595 9600 9605			9609 9614 9619			9624 9628 9633			0 1 1	2 2 3	3 4 4
92	·9638	9643 9647 9652			9657 9661 9666			9671 9675 9680			0 1 1	2 2 3	3 4 4
93	·9685	9689 9694 9699			9703 9708 9713			9717 9722 9727			0 1 1	2 2 3	3 4 4
94	·9731	9736 9741 9745			9750 9754 9759			9763 9768 9773			0 1 1	2 2 3	3 4 4
95	·9777	9782 9786 9791			9795 9800 9805			9809 9814 9818			0 1 1	2 2 3	3 4 4
96	·9823	9827 9832 9836			9841 9845 9850			9854 9859 9863			0 1 1	2 2 3	3 4 4
97	·9868	9872 9877 9881			9886 9890 9894			9899 9903 9908			0 1 1	2 2 3	3 4 4
98	·9912	9917 9921 9926			9930 9934 9939			9943 9948 9952			0 1 1	2 2 3	3 4 4
99	·9956	9961 9965 9969			9974 9978 9983			9987 9991 9996			0 1 1	2 2 2	3 3 4

Index